Top 50 tractors:
1940-1980

Published by

KELSEY PUBLISHING GROUP

Printed in England by William Gibbons
of Willenhall, West Midlands
on behalf of
Kelsey Publishing Limited
Cudham Tithe Barn
Cudham
Kent TN16 3AG
Telephone: 01959 541444
Fax: 01959 541400
www.kelsey.co.uk

©2009
ISBN 978 1 873098 99 8

Acknowledgements
Our thanks go to Scott Lambert for writing and designing the content that makes up this book.

Our appreciation to Stuart Millson, Martin Oldaker, Peter D Simpson and Alan Turner for proof reading.

Also our thanks to Jane Brooks, Lorraine Chippendale, Gary Connolly, Julian Cooksley, Gina Harvey, Kim Jackson, Chris Jaworski, Scott Lambert, Joseph Lewis, Chris McCullough, Orry Mitchell, Tony Nyquist, Kim Parks, Peter Plehov, Stephen Richmond, Howard Sherren, Peter D Simpson, Paul Tofield, Bob Weir, Jonathan Whitlam and Steve Wright for allowing us to use their photographs.

More than 5500 parts and all genuine

Keep it that way

Genuine John Deere parts ensure genuine John Deere performance and reliability.

Visit your local John Deere dealer. Insist on genuine John Deere parts and count on the performance and reliability you expect.

John Deere value you can trust – it's priceless.

And in case you were wondering – there really are more than 5500 parts in a John Deere 6430 tractor.

www.JohnDeere.co.uk

Introduction

Compiling a book about tractors is no easy task, as I am sure you can imagine. At *Tractor & Machinery* though, we come into contact with notable machines every day – which does make things a little easier.

The magazine is well-known for its coverage of agricultural machinery from 1940 to 1980, and so we decided that it would be a good idea to highlight 50 possible landmark machines that were available to farmers and contractors during that period.

This inevitably means that some of the tractors included will have been introduced in the 1930s, but were nevertheless on sale at dealerships in 1940.

You may be wondering just what makes a good tractor and what merits its inclusion in this book?

Naturally, sales volume isn't always an accurate indicator – although demand for a great tractor will invariably mean that vast numbers are built. On the other hand, a tractor may have been produced in large numbers – but poor build quality and basic design flaws may have meant that it would gain a reputation as something of a white elephant.

Generally, a tractor or crawler makes it into the book for a combined 'score' of its cost, features, reliability and performance, but some will inevitably make the cut perhaps on just one or two of these points. For example, the mass-produced Massey Ferguson 135 was competitively priced with a brilliant three-cylinder engine and an excellent hydraulic system, while the Marshall MP6 gained its reputation for being an excellent lugging tractor thanks to the brute force of its Leyland engine.

Throughout the book we have provided a description of what makes each machine a worthy entry, along with basic specifications – to give you the opportunity to see how one tractor stacks up against another.

There will, of course, be machines absent from these pages, as well as some featured here that raise a few eyebrows – particularly for those of you that are loyal to a specific brand. But that will just serve to fuel the debate that rages at rallies and working days across the land! ◼

Contents

1943 saw another change to the A – it gained a larger engine with higher compression, enabling it to produce just over 34hp at the drawbar

John Deere A

Waterloo, Iowa, USA: 1934-1952

The model A was introduced as a replacement for the popular model GP and is seen as one of the great American tractor success stories – and, as such, is a fitting way to begin a book such as this. There aren't many tractors that can claim to be iconic, but the John Deere A is certainly one of them – with its two-cylinder horizontal engine, distinctive styling and simple livery it has certainly stood the test of time.

There were many different variations of the A – 14 in fact – including wide front and orchard models, but all were popular and well-liked by those that operated them. It was always intended that the tractor would be a heavy-duty row-crop machine made for large-scale operations and, in a bid not to lose out to International Harvester in the sales war, Deere decided to emblazon the tractor with a General Purpose decal – in a similar vein to IH's Farmall.

Among the most common configurations were AN (narrow tread), ANH (narrow with high axle), AW (wide tread), AWH (wide with high axle), AR (regular) and AO (orchard) – although a number of AI (industrial) models were produced between 1936 and 1941.

With the likes of Ferdinand Porsche and Raymond Loewy both having a strong input into tractor design, Deere

achieved on the road – almost double the previous achievable top speed.

Despite many of the other tractor manufacturers using four-cylinder engines, Deere retained the two-cylinder format until the end of the 30 series. The distinctive sound generated by these engines earned them the nicknames 'Pop Pops' and 'Johnny Poppers'. The beauty of this engine was that it would run on almost any fuel, more effectively than a four or six-cylinder unit – this was particularly important during the war years, when petrol was rationed and farmers had to rely on whatever cheap fuel they could lay their hands on.

Towards the end of production, the pressed-steel seat was replaced by a sumptuous padded version, headlights were added and the steering shaft now disappeared beneath the bonnet, rather than remaining exposed from steering wheel to steering box. The air intake and exhaust were made shorter and of larger diameter and were also placed in-line so as to aid visibility.

The model A, with obvious exceptions, had the capability to operate with mid-mounted equipment, such as hoes. These were predominantly used on tractors with a V-twin front-wheel configuration, but standard four-wheel machines permitted the use of such implements due to the fact the front axle was positioned in front of the radiator.

Although not as popular as the smaller model B, the John Deere A was much-loved by farmers and over 300,000 units were sold during an 18-year production period. ■

Technical specification

Produced:	1934-1952
Engine:	John Deere
Cylinders:	2
Bore x stroke:	5.5in x 6.5in
	5.5in x 6.75in
Displacement:	309cu in
	321cu in
Torque:	Unknown
	Unknown
Horsepower:	24.7hp
	38hp
Transmission:	4 forward, 1 reverse
	6 forward, 1 reverse
Speed range:	2.3mph – 6.3mph
	2.5mph – 12mph
Linkage:	Drawbar only
	(power lift optional on later models)
Lift capacity:	N/A
Weight:	A: 3,675lbs
	Styled A: 3,817lbs
Tyre sizes:	Front: 5.50x16
	Rear: 11.25x36 or 11x38

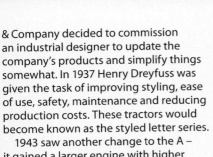

With its good lugging characteristics, the model A was perfect for primary cultivations. Photo: Jonathan Whitlam

& Company decided to commission an industrial designer to update the company's products and simplify things somewhat. In 1937 Henry Dreyfuss was given the task of improving styling, ease of use, safety, maintenance and reducing production costs. These tractors would become known as the styled letter series.

1943 saw another change to the A – it gained a larger engine with higher compression, enabling it to produce just over 34hp at the drawbar. This was a significant increase on the previous incarnation of the tractor. Electric starting was also now standard and a six-speed transmission meant that 12mph could be

The styled version of the model A was introduced in 1938. Photo: Jonathan Whitlam

The tractor was designed to pull a single-furrow plough on the drawbar, but its excellent ground clearance and torque tube transmission enabled mid-mounted implements to be used to great effect

A restored Allis-Chalmers B with straight front axle at a working event. Photo: Paul Tofield

Allis-Chalmers B

West Allis, USA, & Southampton, UK: 1937-1957

Back in the 1930s, farms were still very small and relied heavily on horses. An innovative designer, by the name of Brooks Stevens, could see that there was a gap in the market for a small, low-horsepower tractor that could cater for the needs of such farms – and so he designed the now legendary Allis-Chalmers B.

Fabrication of the model B started in 1937 and would continue for 20 years in the United States, with construction in Great Britain ending in 1955.

The pint-sized A-C was quite unlike any other tractor of the period, as it featured the innovative and patented torque tube chassis. This was a narrow cylinder that transferred power from the engine to the gearbox, as well as housing a shaft that could be coupled to a power take-off. The

beauty of this arrangement was that it used few raw materials – and so was cheap to produce, whilst being slender enough for the operator to have excellent visibility when undertaking row-crop work.

The early American-built tractors also featured a curious, bow-type front axle, but this was superseded in 1945 by a straight, adjustable version. Potato Special and Asparagus versions were offered in the United States with a variation of the bow axle, but all of the model Bs built in Britain had a straight axle.

Innovative is the word that really epitomises the diminutive A-C B, as its clever design meant that it could undertake a vast number of jobs around the farm with relative ease. The tractor was designed to

Technical specification

Produced:	1937-1957
Engine:	Waukesha petrol/tvo
	Allis-Chalmers BE petrol/tvo
	Allis-Chalmers CE petrol
Cylinders:	4
Bore x stroke:	Waukesha: 3in x 4in
	A-C BE: 3.25in x 3.5in
	A-C CE: 3.375in x 3.5in
Displacement:	Waukesha: 113cu in
	A-C BE: 116cu in
	A-C CE: 125cu in
Torque:	Waulkesha: Unknown
	A-C BE: Unknown
	A-C-CE: Unknown
Horsepower:	Waulkesha: 10hp
	A-C BE: 16hp
	A-C CE: 23hp
Transmission:	3 forward, 1 reverse
	(later replaced by 4 forward, 1 reverse)
Speed range:	3f, 1r: 2.75mph – 8.5mph
	4f, 1r: 2.75mph – 10.2mph
Linkage:	Category I (where fitted)
Lift capacity:	Unknown
Weight:	2,060lbs
Tyre sizes:	Front: 4.00x15
	Rear: 9.5x24 or 11.2x24

Alison Robb with her beautifully-restored Allis-Chalmers B. Photo: Bob Weir

This model B has the bow-type front axle and adjustable front wheels. Photo: Paul Tofield

pull a single-furrow plough on the drawbar, but its excellent ground clearance and torque tube transmission enabled mid-mounted implements to be used to great effect. Allis-Chalmers produced a large range of implements for the tractor, but the plough, mid-mounted mower and mid-mounted toolbar were the most popular.

Hydraulics were never really considered in the design of the B, with the raising and lowering of implements controlled by hand-operated levers, but later tractors featured either a primitive single-acting ram or twin-ram arrangement for lifting the drawbar. From 1951, tractors produced in Britain incorporated an Allis-Chalmers-designed three-point linkage, but the low power of the machine meant that it was incapable of operating large implements anyway.

Despite the beginnings of the demise of petrol and tvo power in tractors, A-C at no stage offered a diesel engine for the B – but this never did deter farmers. Being of relatively low horsepower and aimed at small farmers, diesel conversions were uncommon – but some companies saw the opportunity that the tractor presented in terms of other conversions.

Allis-Chalmers offered the IB in America – an industrial variant, with production figures below 3,500 units – but never felt it necessary to produce an orchard or vineyard model. A small number of dealers and engineering companies in Britain seized this opportunity and produced a handful of adapted tractors on demand. An orchard version was achieved by turning the final drive castings by 90 degrees, altering the kingpins on the front axle and modifying the brake rods, steering and seating. This lowered the tractor by approximately 10in and shortened the wheelbase – making it the ideal machine for working under low branches and turning in confined spaces.

Many owners adapted the tractor to their own needs, but the vast majority found that the little Allis was more than suitable in standard configuration. Its versatility and brilliant design made it the ideal tractor for the small farm – a point emphasised by the fact that in excess of 125,000 tractors were built on both sides of the Atlantic. ■

A few D2 5U tractors were fitted with Birtley bulldozing equipment and Caterpillar No 44 hydraulic control plus the Hyster towing winch attached to the rear. Photo: Paul Tofield

Caterpillar D2

Peoria, Illinois, USA: 1938-1957

Although not the most famous of Caterpillar's prestigious product line, the D2 was certainly important to the company's fortunes – as it was one of the only machines to be targeted at the agricultural sector. Unlike many of Caterpillar's bigger crawlers, the little D2 was intended to be a hit in the fields rather than the quarries – and a hit it was!

This is not to say that the D2 didn't appear in construction settings, but primary cultivation was its bread and butter work – where its frugal engine and reliable build quality won many farmers over. Incidentally, the D2 was the smallest diesel crawler that Caterpillar ever built – the R2 model was the spark-ignition engined version of the D2.

The D2 began life in 3J (40-inch track gauge) and 5J (50-inch track gauge) forms with Caterpillar's 31.5hp four-cylinder unit

under the bonnet. It was an impressive-looking machine that had a rear-mounted fuel tank as standard. Side-mounted tanks were an option, but as operators had a tendency to spill fuel on the seat when filling the tank from cans – it was the side-mounted tanks that quickly became standard.

It turned out to be extremely popular with in excess of 19,000 sold in the first nine years – quite remarkable when you consider that the world was at war and none were built at all in 1943.

The biggest change came in 1947 when the D2 received an engine upgrade and new radiator housing, as well as new designations. The 3J was now the 4U and the 5J became the 5U. The D311 powerplant pushed out 38hp at the belt and 32hp at the drawbar. The little Cat would eventually see further power upgrades, first to 38hp at the belt and then to 42hp. Many of the first U series models had side-mounted diesel tanks, but by the end of

production the rear-mounted tanks became standard – as most operators now filled from tanks and not cans, so spillage was largely a thing of the past. Without the side tanks, access to the operator's platform and visibility were vastly improved.

The vast majority of D2s were sold in America but, largely thanks to the Lend-Lease scheme, many D2s appeared on British farms. Latterly, Jack Olding and Levertons would ensure that many more Caterpillars would find their way to Britain when they set up their dealerships, cementing the presence of the yellow tracked machines for years to come. Olding, foolishly, would later relinquish the Caterpillar dealership in favour of Vickers machines – which, as fate would have it, would turn out to be the inferior brand!

Due to the combination of ample horsepower and substantial traction, the Cat was often paired up with large, single-furrow ploughs or disc harrows for land reclamation and winter ploughing, but was equally at home on more delicate duties. Caterpillar was quick to realise the potential of the D2 in more restrained environments and designed an orchard model that was ideal for working among low-hanging fruit trees. The diesel tank was placed behind the bonnet and

Technical specification

Produced:	1938-1957
Engine:	Caterpillar D3400
	Caterpillar D311
Cylinders:	4
Bore x stroke:	D3400: 3.75in x 5in
	D311: 4in x 5in
Displacement:	D3400: 221cu in
	D311: 252cu in
Torque:	D3400: 124lb ft @1,060rpm
	D311: 165lb ft @1,400rpm
Horsepower:	D3400: 31hp
	D311: 38hp
Transmission:	5 forward, 1 reverse
Speed range:	1.7mph – 5.1mph
Linkage:	Drawbar only
Lift capacity:	N/A
Weight:	5U model (1954): 7,600lbs
Track sizes:	12in

Built in 1938 this early example of the 3J D2 came with the seat diesel tank as standard. Photo: Paul Tofield

the seat was positioned over the drawbar, forcing the operator to peer around the bonnet and over the beautifully-curved track guards to see where he was going.

Caterpillar's D2 managed to retain its popularity, largely thanks to the fact it was reliable and was inexpensive to run, with many farmers opting to keep their machines rather than trade them in. Many can still be found in their working clothes with a set of Cambridge rolls working down the ploughed land, whilst some are occasionally put to work with a small set of disc harrows for nostalgia's sake. The little Cat also now finds itself in favour with match ploughmen as it's the perfect machine for pulling a trailed plough.

Despite the earliest D2s being built over 70 years ago, they have managed to retain their charm and purposeful looks and always manage to capture an admiring glance or two from vintage machinery enthusiasts – they were and still are fantastic compact crawlers. ∎

The little Cat also now finds itself in favour with match ploughmen

The U series D2, introduced in 1947, took the transmission and chassis from the previous J series model – but it was now powered by a new design of cross-flow engine. Photo: Paul Tofield

This VAK1 would have sold for £259 in 1940. Photo: Paul Tofield

David Brown VAK1

Meltham Mills, UK: 1939-1945

The Vehicle Agricultural Kerosene 1 was the first tractor to be built by David Brown Tractors that was solely of David Brown design. It followed extensive research carried out by the company into what British farmers really wanted from a tractor – this at a time when the firm was responsible for the production of the Ferguson Model A or Ferguson-Brown.

The tractor made its first appearance at the Royal Show in 1939, alongside the Model A, immediately making an impact due to its Hunting Pink livery. Approximately 3,000 orders for the new tractor were taken at the show but, due to the outbreak of World War II, the newly on-line Meltham Mills factory was needed for the war effort and so it would be several years before the tractors reached their intended recipients.

It was the war that brought about some of the first changes to the design of the new machine, in that the first tractors were produced with a cast-iron radiator grille – but the models that were produced during wartime restrictions ended up with a piece of rolled sheet steel with round holes cut into it. This was to become known as the bullet hole grille.

When normality resumed after the war years, it was instantly noticeable that the VAK1 was far superior to the opposition – which was predominantly Fordson's 25hp Model N. It only had a drawbar and was woefully underpowered, while the four-cylinder, overhead-valve David Brown engine produced 35hp and had the added advantage of a three-point linkage.

Compared to the Fordson it was a much more streamlined machine, helped by its engine screens and now-famous 'scuttle'. The driver sat to the right-hand side, on a bench-type seat with back rest, giving him a commanding view for row-crop work, whilst controls fell easily to hand. It also had the added advantage of having electric starting as an option – a real coup for 1939.

One of the key points that separated the VAK1 from its rivals was the ease with which it could be adjusted, maintained and repaired. It was designed to be simple to look after and achieved this by incorporating a number of useful features, many of which were patented, such as the dished wheel centres which allowed for easy track width change.

The tractor was also designed around a cast-iron chassis that carried the engine and transmission. This, amongst other things, facilitated the removal of the clutch plate without having to split the tractor. It was also possible to remove the transmission's top cover and extract the gearbox and final drive components.

As well as its superior fuel economy compared to the Fordson N, the Brown engine had that added advantage of having replaceable cylinder liners. This avoided the need for an expensive re-bore and oversize pistons when the motor became worn out. It is thought that the VAK1 was the first mass-produced tractor to incorporate wet-liner technology in its engine.

David Brown had close links with engine designers in the car industry, which stood it in good stead when it set about designing an engine for the VAK1, although the 2,523cc unit wasn't without its problems. The heatshield was of a poor design and only half-covered the manifold, meaning that it was a long time before the engine could be switched over to run on tvo. It was also common for the tractor to run ➡

Technical specification

Produced:	1939-1945
Engine:	David Brown
Cylinders:	4
Bore x stroke:	3.5in x 4.0in
Displacement:	154cu in
Torque:	Unknown
Horsepower:	35hp
Transmission:	4 forward, 1 reverse
Speed range:	1.7mph – 15.6mph
Linkage:	Category I
Lift capacity:	Unknown
Weight:	3,472lbs
Tyre sizes:	Front: 4.50x10 or 6.00x19
	Rear: 9x24 or 9x28

... models that were produced during wartime restrictions ended up with a piece of rolled sheet steel with round holes cut into it. This was to become known as the bullet hole grille

DAVID BROWN

JL 7615

Although technically a VAK1, this tractor features many VAK1A modifications. Also notice the different type of David Brown badge to the tractor on the opposite page. Photo: Paul Tofield

*A factory photograph of a partly-assembled
VAK 1 showing the cast mainframe.
Photo: Courtesy of Paul Tofield*

unevenly at low speeds and when not under load. These problems were recognised by engineers at David Brown and later engines received a re-designed manifold and heat shield to combat the switchover problem.

David Brown learned greatly from producing the 5,300 VAK1 tractors during the war years and was able to refine its already-good machine with some subtle, but innovative, design features. Production of the VAK1A began in 1945 and included a baffle that helped to speed the changeover from petrol to tvo, a new air-intake design – that originated from the manifold and helped vaporise the tvo more quickly – and a turnbuckle-type top link; now standard on all tractors. The most obvious changes, though, were the switch from a tubular-style front axle to a square-type and a new pressed steel radiator grille with horizontal apertures.

The original VAK1 design continued to be refined throughout the VAK1A's production until the Cropmaster VAK1C emerged in 1947. This was the culmination of 10 years' experience of building tractors for all manner of applications and was, in essence, the ultimate VAK1.

Despite looking rather like its predecessors, the VAK1C incorporated some interesting advances – the main innovation being the offset engine and gearbox. These were positioned two inches to the side to enable greater traction on the land wheel – a small difference that had a big effect.

Besides smaller cosmetic changes, the Cropmaster had a new two-piece mainframe, a choice of four or six-speed gearboxes and larger mudguards covering 28-inch wheels.

In 1949, a diesel-engined Cropmaster appeared and many earlier tractors were retro-fitted with the new 34hp oil burner, adding a new dimension to an already good machine. Other variants appeared over the years, including the Vineyard Cropmaster, which was a 54-inch wide version of the standard tractor; the Prairie Cropmaster, a diesel-powered machine

aimed at the North American and Canadian markets and the Super Cropmaster, which featured a higher-revving, larger-bored version of David Brown's diesel engine. All in all, nearly 60,000 Cropmasters were built at Meltham, adding to the almost 9,000 VAK1s and 1As built previously.

The VAK1 and its derivatives are very under-rated tractors and were, in fact, some of the most technologically-advanced tractors of their time. The diesel models, in particular are nice to drive and make an attractive and interesting addition to any collection. ∎

*The drawbar frame has the parallel
lower links bolted to it when the arms
are not in use. Photo: Paul Tofield*

... its long-stroke engine gave it excellent pulling power for ploughing, whilst its long wheelbase and easily-adjusted track width made it a stable and practical tractor for working among the crops

Jim Purdie's Farmall M with a wonderful backdrop of rural Scotland. Photo: Bob Weir

Farmall M

Rock Island, USA, Doncaster, UK, & Geelong, Australia: 1939-1954

sk anyone to name an American tractor and the Farmall M will virtually always appear in the top five. Its physical presence is enough to cement it in people's minds, but its unique styling and renowned performance enthrone the model among the top fifty.

It emerged from the Rock Island factory in Illinois as a genuine row crop alternative to the McCormick-Deering W-6 – a highly-successful tractor in its own right. As was the case with most American tractors of the time, it was a petrol-powered machine that relied on a drawbar to do the work – which was more than ample at the time of its launch.

It quickly became a favourite with farmers – its long-stroke engine gave it excellent pulling power for ploughing, whilst its long wheelbase and easily-adjusted track width made it a stable and practical tractor for working among the crops. A high-clearance version was available – the MV – for working among vegetable crops, but this was never sold in Britain.

Anyone who has ever had the pleasure of driving an M will also tell you that another key feature is its speed – it's quick! Obviously the large rear wheels contribute to this, but it also has a very high top gear for transport – which certainly does what it is supposed to. It also has a very upright driving position – one that is shared with the other tractors in the Raymond Loewy-designed letter series. The steering wheel is almost vertical in alignment, forcing the operator to adapt his style slightly to conform with the tractor. This upright stance certainly doesn't feel natural at first, but it soon becomes quite comfortable and is very good for maintaining a straight back.

The M was, of course, the model that put International Harvester Great Britain on the tractor-producing map, in that it was the first to be built at the Wheatley Hall Road site. Other tractors and implements had been assembled from crates as early as the late 1930s, but the British-built M (BM) was the first McCormick IH tractor to be part-manufactured and assembled in Doncaster.

Production of the petrol/tvo model commenced in 1949, ten years after it began in the United States, but it was only three years before it was joined by a diesel alternative – the BMD. In 1953 the Super BM and Super BMD emerged as uprated versions of their respective predecessors, but the most important thing to note was that they were completely British-made.

Throughout its long production run, particularly in Britain, the M series of tractors underwent numerous changes including glow-plug-assisted starting for diesel-engined tractors and live hydraulic linkage – turning the original M into a true force to be reckoned with.

It was, in fact, the BMD that spawned the arrival of the well-respected BD-264 diesel engine. This CAV fuel injection-equipped unit went on to see service in many other renowned IH machines, including the BWD-6 tractor and BTD-6 crawler, both important machines in the history of IHGB.

The model M and its derivatives, be they American, British or Australian in origin, are much-loved tractors – but are not as common at events as their IH stablemates. This is largely due to the fact that they are such heavy tractors to transport, but this doesn't deter enthusiasts, with many in preservation all over the world. Well over a quarter-of-a-million were built in various guises, making the M a true heavyweight in tractor production. ∎

Technical specification

Produced:	1939-1954
Engine:	IH C-248
Cylinders:	4
Bore x stroke:	3.875in x 5.25in
Displacement:	248cu in
Torque:	Unknown
Horsepower:	33hp
Transmission:	5 forward, 1 reverse
Speed range:	2.6mph – 16.3mph
Linkage:	Drawbar only
Lift capacity:	N/A
Weight:	4,858lbs
Tyre sizes:	Front: 6.00x16
	Rear: 11.25x36

IH dealers' demonstration machines were painted white to make them stand out in a crowd. Photo: Peter D Simpson

... the LA was the last of the true standard, petrol-engined tractors built by the company – a true legend in its own right

The Case LA's Flambeau Red and silver livery set the tractor apart from its rivals. Photo: Paul Tofield

Case LA

Racine, Wisconsin, USA: 1940-1953

There's no doubt that the L Series was a real success story as far as Case was concerned. It was introduced in 1929 and was in production until 1940, during which time over 30,000 units were built. Its replacement had to be good – very good – and so a great deal of thought was put into the new machine. Before it was officially launched, some speculated that the new range would be called the M Series – just as the D had replaced the C the year before. In fact, the new tractor would be called the LA.

At first it can be quite confusing, as the LA is a series – as well as one of the models in the series. The model LA was a standard-tread machine, that would later be accompanied by the LA/LPG, an LPG-powered version of the standard tractor; the LAI, an industrial version; the LAIM, a military spec industrial machine; the LAH, a diesel-powered standard tractor, and the LAIH, an industrial-spec machine with a diesel engine.

In reality the LA was an updated version of the outgoing L Series, but featured a four-speed gearbox and elegant styling, painted in the now-familiar Flambeau Red. The engine was remarkably similar to its predecessor's in that it operated at the same speed and shared the same bore and stroke – with a choice of gasoline or low-cost fuel as power.

It would be another two years before Case introduced a diesel-powered version of the LA. The LAH was so called because it used a Hesselman design. Swedish engineer, Jonas Hesselman, pioneered the use of such engines in the 1920s and they went on to be used in buses, lorries and eventually tractors. A Hesselman engine is essentially a fuel-injected, spark-ignition engine that has been converted to run on heavier oil-based products – in this case, diesel. The advantages of such a design were clear – diesel was cheaper than petrol and the engine could be smaller than a rival diesel engine of the period – saving money on manufacturing costs.

Having said this, the Hesselman design had a reputation for emitting clouds of

Technical specification

Produced:	1940-1953
Engine:	J.I. Case
Cylinders:	4
Bore x stroke:	4.625in x 6in
Displacement:	403.2cu in
Torque:	Unknown
Horsepower:	58.5hp
Transmission:	4 forward, 1 reverse
Speed range:	2.5mph – 10.8mph
Linkage:	Drawbar only
Lift capacity:	N/A
Weight:	7,621lbs
Tyre sizes:	Front: 7.50x18
	Rear: 14x30

The LA was a handsome beast - accentuated by its design detail. Photo: Jonathan Whitlam

exhaust smoke and the concept never really caught on. Throughout the production life of the LA, fewer than 500 diesel models were built from a total of over 35,000.

In a bid to make the LA more appealing to cash-conscious farmers, the LA/LPG was introduced in 1952. Liquid Petroleum Gas was cheaper than petrol in the main, but was difficult to store safely and so very few farmers made the switch from petrol to LPG.

A significant options list also helped to persuade farmers to buy the LA. These included: pto, electric starting and lighting, exhaust silencer and hydraulic controls. Some of these would become standard towards the end of production, while

refinements were constantly made to the basic design to improve what was fundamentally a very good tractor. Its engine was renowned for its ability to pull well, with the tractor easily coping with a four-furrow plough – helping it to remain one of Case's most popular tractors for many years.

The 1950s was the decade that saw diesel really take off as a tractor fuel and so it was inevitable that Case would have to take this into consideration. As fate

would have it though, the long-running LA would never be powered by a true diesel – that honour would be bestowed to the Desert Sunset-liveried 500 model. Case had taken the LA as far as it could, but the tractor remained a firm favourite for many years. Petrol-powered models would be built for the next 15 years or so, but the LA was the last of the true standard, petrol-engined tractors built by the company – a true legend in its own right. ■

When your tractor looks as good as this LA does, why re-paint it? Photo: Paul Tofield

The late John Graham aboard his stunning W-9. Photo: Gina Harvey

McCormick-Deering W-9

Milwaukee, Wisconsin, USA: 1940-1953

Some impressive beasts graced British shores thanks to the Lend-Lease scheme – and the McCormick-Deering W-9 was certainly one of them. A bruising heavyweight of a machine, the W-9 was only really suitable for the large farm and so went under the radar of many a landowner – but for those who experienced the tractor, it was a machine never to be forgotten.

The first thing to say about the W-9 is that it was a big tractor – quite unlike anything British farmers had ever experienced. American farmers were used to cultivating the prairies with machines of this scale, but it came as a shock when the first of the W-9s arrived to take their place on the British agricultural scene. Weighing in at around 3 tons, the tractor was almost double the weight of the popular Fordson N, but certainly had the power and torque to go with it.

It should be said at this point that the purpose of the W series Standard-badged tractors was heavy fieldwork and primary cultivations in particular, whereas the letter series tractors – like the Farmall M – were designed for inter-row cultivations and had a much 'leaner' appearance.

With its streamlined appearance the big W-9 was certainly a stunning tractor – everything about it was beautifully crafted. It had a sleek look about it, thanks to its considerable length and sculpted tin work – not something you'd usually associate with a tractor of this size. The sculpted fuel tank, bonnet panels and cast chassis framed the engine almost as if it were a work of art.

When the W-9 was first introduced in 1940 it was offered with a choice of three engines: petrol, diesel or all-fuel – with the all-fuel being the standard engine until the petrol variant became standard in 1947.

Unlike its smaller sibling, the W-6, the W-9 wasn't available in orchard guise – but five other models graced the line-up: the WD-9 (diesel), WR-9 and WDR-9 (petrol and diesel models designed for rice applications that featured a hand-operated clutch and larger mudguards) and the I-9 and ID-9 (petrol and diesel-powered industrial versions).

Both the W-4 and W-6 tractors were built at the Rock Island plant in Illinois, home to some very influential tractors over the years, whereas the W-9 rolled out of the factory in Wisconsin. All were popular, with approximately 25,000 of each of the smaller models built, whilst over 67,000 W-9s were manufactured. Most saw use in their homeland, but in the 13-year period that it remained in production a vast number were shipped abroad.

Although most of the W series tractors featured a belt pulley, useful for driving stationary equipment, the W-9 had an added advantage – its bulk. When towing threshing machines from field to field, particularly in undulating areas, they had a tendency to get the better of the towing tractor and jackknife the whole ensemble. The W-9

wasn't immune to this type of scenario, but was more suited to the job than most.

Despite not being advisable to tow equipment and trailers at high speed, the W-9 was a useful tractor if your farm was spread over a wide area. With a governed top speed of 15½mph (many operators claimed that 18mph was a more realistic figure), the tractor took the drudgery out of getting from field to field. There was a large jump between fourth and fifth gears, with top gear only selected for transport, but the W-9 had a well-spaced range of speeds that made it a pleasure to use in the field. The steering was by no means the lightest, but a substantial load on the drawbar helped to bring the nose up, thus reducing the load on the operator's arms.

All in all it was much-loved by those that used one in earnest – a true heavyweight that commanded the utmost respect. If you treated the McCormick-Deering W-9 correctly, it would be everything you could want from a high-horsepower tractor and more. ■

Technical specification

Produced:	1940-1953
Engine:	McCormick-Deering C-335
Cylinders:	4
Bore x stroke:	4.4in x 5.5in
Displacement:	334.5cu in
Torque:	Unknown
Horsepower:	49hp
Transmission:	5 forward, 1 reverse
Speed range:	2.25mph – 15.5mph
Linkage:	Drawbar only
Lift capacity:	N/A
Weight:	6,426lbs
Tyre sizes:	Front: 7.50x18
	Rear: 16x34

It had a sleek look about it, thanks to its considerable length and sculpted tin work – not something you'd usually associate with a tractor of this size

Alistair Taylor's McCormick-Deering W-9 has been converted to diesel. Photo: Bob Weir

*Malcolm Reid aboard his beautifully-restored Mark 1.
Photo: Kim Jackson*

Field-Marshall Mark 1

Gainsborough, UK: 1945-1947

During the early to middle part of the last century, single-cylinder tractors were very common in Europe, with most countries having at least one tractor manufacturer dedicated to building such machines. Landini, Ursus and Société

Française de Materiel Agricole et Industriel de Vierzon (SFV) all looked to the 'king' of single-cylinder tractors, Heinrich Lanz, for inspiration when designing new machines. Marshall of Gainsborough was no exception and flew the flag for British single-cylinder tractor manufacturers.

Following the success of the brilliant model M, Marshall toyed with the idea of

a replacement at least two years before it actually went on sale. Many observers had speculated that the company would abandon the tried and tested single-cylinder engine in favour of a multi-cylinder diesel unit – as was appearing in rival manufacturers' machines. But, as the old adage goes, 'if it ain't broke, don't fix it' and Marshall was right to adopt this policy – the retention of the original engine configuration proved to be the right decision in the short term.

The new tractor, the Mark 1, used an engine of a similar design to the Model M's two-stroke diesel – albeit with an increase in horsepower. This horizontally-orientated unit was extremely miserly on fuel, reliable and performed well under load – and, as a result, proved to be a big hit with cash-conscious farmers.

the jobs for which it was designed.

With its low-rev lugging characteristics, the Mark 1 could pull a four-furrow plough with relative ease, but found particular favour with threshing contractors, who liked the fact the tractor could be left on tick-over all day powering the drum – with the benefit of easier starting compared to the traction engines they had been used to.

Starting, although not exactly key-quick, had always been the model M's strong point. The same method of ignition was retained for the Mark 1 and required the operator to place a lit wick into the cylinder head whilst hand-cranking the engine on half-compression (controlled via a decompressor arm). The first few tractors produced only had this facility, but the vast majority of Mark 1s also had the luxury of cartridge starting.

This was essentially the same principle as a shotgun cartridge and utilised an aperture at the front of the tractor – into which the cartridge was placed. The decompressor was then set, with the engine at top dead centre, and the starter valve on the cylinder head was turned to the appropriate position, before the firing pin was activated – detonating the cartridge. This sent the charge into the cylinder and forced the piston backwards at such a velocity that the engine fired and continued to run.

The engine was designed to run anti-clockwise, but would often run in the opposite direction when it fired. This wasn't particularly a problem in terms of the engine running, but the operator could find out the hard way when he released the clutch and found that he had three reverse speeds, instead of the usual one!

A variant of the Mark 1 was available, aimed to appeal to contractors and local authorities. The Mark 2, as it was officially designated, was better known as the

Technical specification

Produced:	1945-1947
Engine:	Marshall 2-stroke diesel
Cylinders:	1
Bore x stroke:	6.5in x 9in
Displacement:	299cu in
Torque:	Unknown
Horsepower:	38hp
Transmission:	3 forward, 1 reverse
Speed range:	2.75mph – 6mph
(optional 9mph top speed transmission)	
Linkage:	Drawbar only
Lift capacity:	N/A
Weight:	6,500lbs
Tyre sizes:	Front: 6.00x19
	Rear: 11.25x28

Contractors' model and featured the 9mph top gear as standard, along with a canvas canopy, full lighting kit and rear-wheel braking. An extension for the exhaust pipe was also made available, standard on later Mark 2 tractors, to prevent fumes from becoming trapped under the canopy and choking the operator.

Besides being a big hit with the threshing gangs, the Mark 2 also found favour with timber companies. The combination of the tractor and Marshall's own underslung, rear winch allowed trees to be felled in heavily-wooded areas and winched to clearings with relative ease. Unlike the previous incarnation of the winch, fitted to the ➡

It's fair to say that the Mark 1 was remarkably similar to the model M underneath, but took on a more streamlined appearance than its predecessor. The cylinder head was completely enclosed by a shroud that curved both ways to create an elegant outer shell, which looked resplendent in Mid-Brunswick Green with silver trim.

Although the engine lent itself to work in the field, it was never the ideal piece of machinery for transportation purposes. It was far from smooth and wasn't exactly pleasant if travelling large distances between fields – with the added problem of a 6mph top speed (a 9mph third gear option was offered). Most operators inevitably learned to live with this and forgave the tractor, as it made up for it when undertaking

The Mark 1, like all the Field-Marshalls that would follow, was a purposeful-looking machine. Photo: Orry Mitchell

The Mark 1 enjoyed a production life of two years before it was replaced by the Series 2 model at the 1947 Royal Show

Orry Mitchell's tractor pictured at Cregneash village on the Isle of Man. Photo: Orry Mitchell

model M, this one was housed almost entirely under the operator's platform. The other beauty of this particular combination was the hand-operated drum brake that also allowed the winch to be used for towing.

The Mark 1 enjoyed a production life of two years before it was replaced by the Series 2 model at the 1947 Royal Show. The latest incarnation of the proven single-cylinder concept saw the horsepower rating improved to 40hp, wider rear wheels fitted and improved braking – amongst other things.

Significant advances were made after John Fowler & Co Ltd of Leeds became part of the Thomas Ward Group – to which Marshall belonged – in 1946. It wasn't until mid-1947 though that the product of the amalgamation emerged. The Fowler FD5, or VF as it would become, was a tracked version of the Series 2 – with some subtle differences. The VF turned out to be such a popular crawler that Marshall used it as the basis for its next incarnation of its well-liked tractor – the Series 3, launched in 1950.

Evolution of the design continued through to the Series 3A, produced from 1952-56, but by this time the project had run its course and despite refining

the single-cylinder concept almost beyond belief, farmers were demanding multi-cylinder engines in their tractors – something to which Marshall would respond with its MP4 and MP6 tractors.

There are many staunch supporters of Marshall tractors and a large number

of Mark 1 machines can still be found at working days – particularly if you pay close attention to the threshing demonstrations. Their distinctive thudding exhaust note can be heard from long distances, making them a magnet for interested enthusiasts and inquisitive onlookers. ■

Typical work for a Field-Marshall – cutting oats with an Albion binder. Photo: Orry Mitchell

David Ritchie's wonderful 1948 model started life with a petrol/tvo engine, but was later retro-fitted with a P6 diesel. Photo: Bob Weir

Fordson Major E27N

Dagenham, UK: 1945-1952

In a bid to keep abreast of the advances in agricultural technology and to replace the aged model N, the management at Fordson in Britain wanted a new tractor – one that would build on the reputation that the company already enjoyed with British farmers.

Unfortunately this came at a time when economic conditions were difficult, to say the least, as World War II had come to an end and there simply wasn't the money to invest in a 'from-scratch' model at Dagenham. The obvious solution, therefore,

was to build the Ford-Ferguson – a truly modern agricultural machine that couldn't be further apart from the Fordson N. This, however, was still deemed economically unviable and the only option was to upgrade the existing model – again – and so the Major 'England-27hp-N' was born.

The original model N's petrol engine was retained – but upgraded to a high-compression format – but this was generally deemed to be underpowered. Despite its lack of punch, the new tractor was able to operate with a three-furrow plough – largely because the power-sapping, worm-style, final drive was scrapped in favour of a bevel gear system. The fact still

remained, however, that the petrol unit was inadequate and its higher compression meant that it had a limited service life. This was further exacerbated by the fact that it had no cylinder liners and needed to be re-bored when it was worn out.

There was a solution to this problem in the form of Frank Perkins of Peterborough. He had already taken the step of converting his own Fordson with one of his company's diesel engines and to great effect at that. The management at Fordson heard about this and promptly sent some representatives to investigate.

What they discovered had a profound impact – so much so that a deal was struck and Perkins set about supplying Fordson with the venerable P6 six-cylinder power plant. This engine saw use predominantly in commercial vehicles, but proved to farmers that diesel was a viable alternative to petrol when it came to tractors. The performance of the engine helped the cause, as it was able to produce a credible 45hp at a lowly 1,500rpm.

Despite weighing in at 500lb more than its petrol/tvo sister, the P6-powered E27N ➡

David Ritchie's tractor is fitted with a three-point linkage and pto unit. Photo: Bob Weir

quickly gained an excellent reputation for performance – so much so that many petrol models were retro-fitted with the diesel variant. The petrol version's clutch and three-forward, one-reverse transmission were retained, but a beefed-up rear axle was added to cope with the added weight.

As for the business end of the machine, it was equipped with one of two 'bolt-on' options – either a Smith unit, with a single control lever, or a Varley system that had a lever to control the lift and another to operate external slave cylinders.

Over 20,000 E27Ns were built with a factory-fitted P6, proving the machine's new-found popularity with farmers and cementing Fordson's lofty position among tractor manufacturers.

This was, of course, only part of the story – as the E27N skid unit was used to full-effect in the County Full Track

Technical specification

Produced:	1945-1952
Engine:	Fordson petrol/tvo
	Perkins P6 diesel
Cylinders:	Petrol/tvo: 4
	Diesel: 6
Bore x stroke:	Petrol/tvo: 4.125in x 5.0in
	Diesel: 3.5in x 5.0in
Displacement:	Petrol/tvo: 267cu in
	Diesel: 288cu in
Torque:	Petrol/tvo: Unknown
	Diesel: 168lb ft @1,500rpm
Horsepower:	Petrol/tvo: 27hp
	Diesel: 45hp
Transmission:	3 forward, 1 reverse
Speed range:	2.5mph – 5.4mph
Linkage:	Drawbar only
	Optional Category II linkage
Lift capacity:	Unknown
Weight:	4,000lbs
Tyre sizes:	Front: 6.00x19
	Rear: 11x36

A Perkins-powered County Full Track. Photo: Peter D Simpson

The DG4 system was a simple solution to the need for more traction that relied on the tractor's own steering and differential to get it around corners

Andy McMinn's Fordson Major with Roadless DG4 half-track conversion. Photo: Gary Connolly

crawler. The prototype first emerged in 1948 using the petrol/tvo engine and it soon became obvious that it would be a great success in both the agricultural and construction sectors.

As was the case with their wheeled cousins, the crawlers were produced with both engine variants and established themselves as an attractive alternative for those that ploughed in heavy conditions or needed a machine with lower ground pressure – as well as being a powerful dozer.

Roadless Traction of Hounslow also produced a tracked version of the E27N, but this was of the half-track variety and consisted of a bolt-on assembly that

was either specified from new or retro-fitted. The DG4 system was a simple solution to the need for more traction that relied on the tractor's own steering and differential to get it around corners – saving money on what were deemed to be unnecessary steering clutches.

Both County and Roadless used the E27N for their tracked systems until the introduction of the E1A Major, when the companies decided that four-wheel drive versions of standard tractors were the way forward, although County did continue to offer the Full Track in its popular 'Ploughman' guise for some years.

Despite early doubts about its power,

the E27N proved that it had what it took to be a worthy successor to the model N and provided sterling service to farmers, particularly in diesel guise, until the radically-new Major was revealed to dealers and the Press in November 1951.

The E27N now commands a great deal of respect on the rally circuit and machines with factory-fitted P6 engines, both wheeled and tracked, carry a premium when they come up for sale. Finding a good machine in original condition is becoming increasingly difficult, particularly as even the last models are over 55 years-old. If you are lucky enough to purchase one – treasure it as the true piece of history that it is. ∎

Stephen Todd's wonderful TED-20 was restored by Northern Ireland-based David Graham. Photo: Gary Connolly

Ferguson TE-20

Coventry, UK: 1946-1956

If this book had been produced more like a popular music chart than the chronological format in which it appears, then the Ferguson TE-20 would surely occupy the top spot. Quite simply, it was the tractor that revolutionised farming and was the forefather to today's modern behemoths.

It all began as far back as the early 20th century, when a young Harry Ferguson found himself working for the Irish Board of Agriculture – striving to improve the efficiency of tractor usage. He concluded that the problem lay with the over-complicated design and construction of tractors and ploughs. The only conclusion, as far as Ferguson was concerned, was to design his own machinery.

Despite having experience with International Harvester's Mogul and Titan models, Ferguson built his first prototype around an Eros conversion of a Ford model T car. The essence of this combination was that the tractor and plough were as one, with the operator having control of all major functions from the seat.

After many refinements to his design, particularly with a Fordson model F tractor, Ferguson's two-furrow mechanical lift plough was put into production by the Sherman brothers in 1925. The plough was marketed for three years until the discontinuation of the Fordson caused manufacturing to come to a standstill. This didn't deter Ferguson and, in fact, helped to concentrate his mind onto his one true wish – designing his own tractor.

By obtaining components from several different parties, Ferguson was able to produce a tractor at his Belfast premises as early as 1933. The in-house designed three-point linkage was bolted to a David Brown transmission which, in turn, was powered by a Hercules engine – the Black Tractor was born!

This prototype enabled Ferguson to approach manufacturers and convince them that the product he had was viable. As David Brown had supplied the gearbox and several other components, the Huddersfield-based company was the obvious choice for putting the tractor into production and it wasn't long before the two parties reached an agreement for Brown to build the tractors and Ferguson to sell them.

The Type A's design closely resembled the Black Tractor's design, but used a 20hp Coventry Climax engine and was finished in a battleship grey livery – which Ferguson resisted at first. Around 1,200 tractors were built, accompanied by a limited selection of five implements: single and two-furrow ploughs, spring and rigid-tine cultivators and a ridger.

After two years of production, much was learnt about the tractor's fundamental problems – one of which was the woefully under-powered engine. David Brown worked hard to convince Ferguson that the tractor should be more powerful, but Ferguson would have none of it and the two parties went their separate ways – with Brown opting to build the VAK 1 and Ferguson looking for a new manufacturer. The key was that Ferguson still held the patent for the draft control system and so any tractor he managed to put into production would be superior to the VAK 1.

By demonstrating the Type A to Henry Ford, Ferguson was able to convince the motoring giant to build the tractor – resulting in production models being presented to farmers as early as June 1939. The new tractor, designated the Ford 9N, was an instant success in America but technicalities in the agreement between Ford and Ferguson meant that the tractor could not be built by Ford in Britain. A combination of the death of Henry Ford, World War II and the introduction of Henry Ford II as chairman of the Ford Motor Company led to problems, forcing Ferguson to look for another manufacturer in Britain to build his tractor. Step forward Sir John Black of the Standard Motor Company.

Following the war, many of the big players in the automotive industry were searching for ways to make use of their factories and Standard's Banner Lane plant was lying empty after being used to make aeroplane engines. Sir John saw this as the ideal opportunity to fill the production gap – this is where the Ferguson TE-20 we have come to know and love first appeared.

The Tractor England 20hp (TE-20) looked like the 9N, albeit with a different bonnet assembly and a Continental Z-120 engine, as opposed to the Mercury V8-derived unit used in the Ford. The tractor was well-received by farmers, but two problems would initially cause problems; petrol rationing and the fact that the Ferguson System relied on purpose-built implements if it were to be used to its full potential.

The latter was quickly rectified when a network of implement manufacturers was brought on-line to build the multitude of tools that would become as iconic as the tractor itself.

Harry Ferguson had always favoured petrol as a tractor fuel, but the excise duty associated with it meant that it wasn't a viable option. Luckily, Standard was developing an engine for its new saloon car and after discussions with the Ministry of Transport, Sir John Black was able to ensure that the engine would be available for the tractor. The new petrol engine brought about a different designation for the tractor, the TEA-20 – but more importantly, with further development, would enable the tractor to run on tractor vaporising oil (tvo) – a fuel not subject to excise duty. This new, dual-fuelled model was called the TED-20.

The year was 1951 and although a viable alternative to a straight petrol model, the TED-20 was coming up against more and more diesel-engined competitors. The only option was to introduce a diesel variant. Ferguson hated the idea, but realised it had to be done if the tractor were to be a dominant force. A Perkins P3 was considered, but was deemed too ➡

Scott and Dale Lambert's 1951 TED-20 is seen here with the most popular Ferguson implement of them all – the two-furrow plough. Photo: Scott Lambert

Technical specification

Produced:	1946-1956
Engine:	Continental Z-120 petrol
	Standard petrol, tvo, lamp oil & diesel
	Perkins P3 diesel (conversion)
Cylinders:	Continental: 4
	Standard: 4
	Perkins: 3
Bore x stroke:	Cont: 3.188in x 3.74in
	Std petrol/tvo (early): 3.149in x 3.62in
	Std petrol/tvo (late): 3.346in x 3.62in
	Standard diesel: 3.187in x 4in
	Perkins diesel: 3.5in x 5in
Displacement:	Continental: 120cu in
	Standard petrol/tvo (early): 112.9cu in
	Standard petrol/tvo (late): 127.4cu in
	Standard diesel: 127.6cu in
	Perkins diesel: 144cu in
Torque:	Continental: Unknown
	Standard petrol/tvo (early): Unknown
	Standard petrol/tvo (late): Unknown
	Standard diesel: Unknown
	Perkins diesel: 88lb ft @1,300rpm
Horsepower:	Continental: 23.9hp
	Standard petrol/tvo (early): 23.9hp
	Standard petrol/tvo (late): 28.2hp
	Standard diesel: 26hp
	Perkins diesel: 34hp
Transmission:	4 forward, 1 reverse
Speed range:	2.49mph – 13.24mph
Linkage:	Category I
Lift capacity:	992lbs
Weight:	Cont: 2,500lbs
	Std petrol/tvo: 2,535lbs
	Std diesel: 2,701lbs
	Perkins diesel: Unknown
Tyre sizes:	Front: 4.00x19
	Rear: 10x28

Quite simply, the tractor was a revelation and would go on to form the basis of several iconic agricultural machines…

The TE-20, in all its guises, is very popular at ploughing matches – with many events having a dedicated Ferguson class. Photo: Scott Lambert

powerful and too expensive and so a Standard unit was developed that would also find its way into the Vanguard car. The latest tractor was designated the TEF-20.

Although Ferguson had realised the potential for narrow versions of his petrol and tvo-engined tractors in orchard and vineyard environments, it was the advent of diesel that helped to propel the tractor to the status that it would eventually enjoy. More and more tractors were being used in industrial environments and so Ferguson and Standard were quick to produce versions that were almost tailor-made to customers' needs. By the time production ceased in 1956, 16 different models had been offered and over 500,000 Standard-built tractors had been produced at Banner Lane!

Prior to the introduction of the Ferguson System, farmers believed that power and mass were the key, but the lightweight TE-20 proved that with the appropriate weight transfer from the implement, a low-horsepower machine could perform as well, if not better, than a bigger tractor.

The fundamental principles aside, the tractor incorporated radical features that would make life easier and safer for the operator. Easily-adjustable track settings, independent brakes, straightforward controls and ease of maintenance were all important – but innovative features,

such as using the gear lever to start the machine, were key elements that ensured farmers wouldn't injure themselves.

Quite simply, the tractor was a revelation and would go on to form the basis of several iconic agricultural machines such as the

ubiquitous Massey Ferguson 35. Technology would obviously progress far beyond what was ever imagined at the TE-20's inception, but the fact that virtually every modern tractor uses the three-point linkage system is testament to Harry Ferguson's foresight. ∎

Peter Harris's TEF-20 is fitted with a front-mounted Ferguson earth mover. Photo: Kim Jackson

Classic Massey
& Ferguson enthusiast

The independent Ferguson and Massey Ferguson magazine

2775 MASSEY FERGUSON MF

News, buyer's guides, product reviews, restorations, letters, auctions and more!

If there was ever a tractor that could be described as muscular, the 744PD is it! Photo: Paul Tofield

Massey-Harris 744PD/744D

Manchester & Kilmarnock, UK: 1948-1953

There are a few tractors that will raise eyebrows because of their inclusion in this book – and the Massey-Harris 744PD is certainly one of them. It may not have sold in vast numbers, but it had a good pedigree and an even better engine. The tractor's limited sales success could be attributed to many different factors, but those that bought it found it to be a capable workhorse and a strong lugger.

Massey-Harris was better known in Britain for its range of implements, although some tractors did appear on British farms in the pre-war years. It wasn't until the Lend-Lease scheme was operational that more M-H tractors began to appear in the UK – built in the company's Canadian and American factories.

It would be 1948 before Massey-Harris tractors were actually 'built' in Britain at the Ashburton Road facility in Manchester. This was essentially a warehouse that, in the first instance, assembled 44 Series tractors from crate form and installed Perkins engines shipped from Peterborough.

There are numerous accounts of what actually happened in terms of production at Manchester, but some reports state that as few as 16 tractors were actually built before production transferred to Kilmarnock in Scotland. Here, tractors were actually put together on a production line – firstly in standard (both long and short wheelbase) and row-crop forms and later in tricycle and general purpose guises. The first tractors were known as 744PDs and later models were called 744Ds, with the '7' signalling British-built, the 'P' denoting Perkins and the 'D', diesel. Perkins engines were used in Britain, while six-cylinder Continental motors were used in the Canadian-built 44s.

The 744 was a purposeful-looking machine with flowing lines accentuated by the sharp-angle tyre tread patterns of the day – it appeared strong, yet 'friendly' at the same time. Most farmers were still utilising trailed implements, as the three-

point linkage had only recently become the vogue, so the 744 was the perfect primary cultivation tool. Large ploughs and cultivators were the order of the day to harness the power generated by the Perkins P6 motor and the traction resulting from plenty of weight over the back.

This is not to say that the 744 didn't have hydraulic capability, it did, but this was woeful in comparison to what would eventually become part of its extended family – the Ferguson TE-20. It was a foot-operated system that was purely what we would now describe as a power

The red and yellow livery, coupled with the black P6 engine creates a nice look. Photo: Paul Tofield

lift – with no draft control or any other sophisticated hydraulic functions. The lift was the perfect accompaniment for the row-crop version, as it was ideal for lifting mid-mounted hoes and the like.

The 744 also found a niche as a good tractor for powering pto-driven implements – as the grunt from the big P6 enabled the operator to maintain a constant speed when undertaking tasks, without having to declutch and let the implement 'catch-up'. As it was a good all-rounder, most tractors were fitted with pneumatic tyres, but steel wheels were also available for those that required extra traction in arduous conditions. Interestingly, a half-track conversion was also offered directly by Massey-Harris, as opposed to the Roadless-built kit used on the Fordson E27N Major.

Production of the under-rated Massey-Harris 744D continued until the merger with Ferguson in 1953, when it was replaced by the Perkins L4-powered 745 model. This tractor was produced for another five years until it was, technically, replaced by the much-loved Massey Ferguson 65 – a different breed of agricultural machine altogether! ◼

Large ploughs and cultivators were the order of the day to harness the power generated by the Perkins P6 motor and the traction resulting from plenty of weight over the back

Technical specification

Produced:	1948-1953
Engine:	Perkins P6
Cylinders:	6
Bore x stroke:	3.5in x 5in
Displacement:	288cu in
Torque:	168lb ft @1,500rpm
Horsepower:	45hp
Transmission:	5 forward, 1 reverse
Speed range:	Std: 2.19mph – 12mph
	Row-crop: 2.48mph – 13.8mph
Linkage:	Category II (where fitted)
Lift capacity:	Unknown
Weight:	Standard: 5,152lbs
	Row-crop: 4,704lbs
Tyre sizes:	Standard: Front: 6.00x19
	Rear: 12.75x28
	Row-crop: Front: 5.50x16
	Rear: 12x38

There is very little at the front of the Lanz, the engine is low in front of the driver and the radiator is side-mounted. Photo: Peter D Simpson

Lanz Bulldog D2206

Mannheim, Germany: 1951-1955

Perhaps the most recognisable and famous of all hot-bulb tractors, the first incarnation of the Lanz Bulldog appeared in 1921, when Heinrich Lanz developed a tractor that had the capability to run on almost any fuel – be it petrol, paraffin or diesel. This was, of course, extremely popular with thrifty farmers and proved so successful that over 200,000 were built before production eventually ceased after the takeover by John Deere in 1955.

The semi-diesel variant first appeared in 1951 and continued the tradition of the single, horizontal cylinder layout. It was a heavy, somewhat crude design but was simple, reliable and most importantly, cheap. It appeared clumsy in comparison with other manufacturers' machines, but was designed primarily for powering threshers and other stationary equipment – not for extensive field work.

The D2206 was one of the new semi-diesel designs and the culmination of Lanz's single-cylinder endeavours. With an 11:1 compression ratio, the engine was unable

to ignite diesel – which meant it had to be started on petrol and switched over to diesel once up and running. Full diesels

Technical specification

Produced:	1951-1955
Engine:	Lanz two-stroke
Cylinders:	1
Bore x stroke:	5.125in x 7.00in
Displacement:	138cu in
Torque:	Unknown
Horsepower:	22hp
Transmission:	6 forward, 2 reverse
Speed range:	1.3mph – 17.0mph
Linkage:	Category I
Lift capacity:	Unknown
Weight:	3,920lbs
Tyre sizes:	Front: 5.50x16
	Rear: 11x28

would eventually follow but by this time John Deere had stamped its authority over tractor design and single-cylinder tractors would be confined to the history books.

The 22hp tractor was essentially the same as the 17hp D1706, but different governor settings enabled it to run faster and produce more power, whilst altering the gearbox ratios allowed Lanz's engineers to give the D2206 added pull. This was the company's policy; to produce a small model first, that would appeal most to farmers, but could then be easily adapted to offer a more powerful tractor. The D2206 produced 22.8hp at the belt and 19.8 at the drawbar – not remarkable by today's standards, but adequate for the type of work it would undertake.

Unlike its predecessors, the D2206 was an electric-start machine, but could be started by hand. Firstly, the system was switched to petrol then the cylinder was primed by operating the injector pump with a hand lever. This doubled as a stop lever and was connected directly to the injection pump. Three to four pumps were required to prime the tractor before starting. The trembler coil was then switched on to supply the spark and the engine rocked backwards and forwards via the hand wheel on the left-hand side of the tractor. Once the engine fired, it was necessary to check that it was running in the correct direction before switching to diesel.

Prior to starting, the right-hand main bearing had to be primed by opening a cap, squirting in oil and opening a tap to

A tractor of this size was ideal for light row-crop cultivation work and grassland duties and an excellent road tractor with a top speed of 17 mph. Photo: Peter D Simpson

let it enter the cylinder and main bearing. It was necessary to have this tap because of pressure in the crankcase. A handle was then inserted through a hole in the flywheel, which was then turned to prime the

lubrication system. In cold weather, paraffin could be added to reduce the viscosity of the oil around the piston – thus aiding starting.

The engine incorporated several innovative features, including a pump to remove any excess oil from the crankcase and the lower of the two transfer ports. This was then returned to the oil tank. Static blades were also present in the exhaust pipe, which made the exhaust gases spin at high speed – causing the oil droplets to be thrown to the outside of the silencer by centrifugal force. This made the Lanz friendlier to drive, as the operator wasn't subjected to the spatters of oil which bedevilled drivers of Field-Marshalls! The oil ran to the bottom of the exhaust, which could then be drained, via a tap, on a regular basis.

Innovation didn't stop at the engine, as the rest of the tractor incorporated features that made driving it a pleasant experience for the operator. A spring and hydraulic damper assembly cushioned the seat, whilst the kingpins were able to slide on a spring-loaded cushion. A foot-operated accelerator was also standard – an interesting feature for the period.

The last Lanz tractors built at Mannheim were produced in John Deere livery, but by 1960 the Lanz name had been completely dropped on export models – remaining on the home-market machines until the mid-1960s. The multi-cylinder diesel tractors that are now the norm were considered the best way to take the company forward, but by that time the thumping power of the single-cylinder engine had helped to cement the Bulldog in agricultural folklore. ∎

Peter Harvey aboard his 1954 Lanz D2206 built at Mannheim, Germany. Photo: Peter D Simpson

Fordson Major E1A

Dagenham, UK: 1952-1958

Fordson's engineers knew when they developed the E27N that the tractor was only ever destined to be a stop-gap and so continued to work towards a more fitting replacement for the model N. The Perkins P6 diesel obviously added a new dimension to the Major, but it was clear that the eventual successor to the N would have to be new from the ground up.

Production of the E27N was still in its infancy when a prototype engine was developed by a promising Ford engineer by the name of Laurie Martland. This engine was the beginning of a standard powerplant that was intended to be built in either petrol, tvo or diesel form. The prototype was shoehorned into a modified E27N, whilst another tractor received a Continental petrol engine for evaluation purposes.

It would be 1949 before a final prototype tractor emerged featuring an all-new six-speed transmission and a diesel version of Markland's revised engine. All three fuel variants utilised the same basic block, but the diesel version had an increased bore. All three used different compression ratings; 5.5:1 for petrol, 4.35:1 for tvo and 16:1 for diesel. The prototype was continually tweaked, with the tin work given the thumbs up in 1950, enabling a handful of tractors to go on field trials and publicity work in 1951, before its eventual public launch at the Smithfield Show in December of that year.

Although the new Major was offered with three engine choices, the diesel was by far and away the most popular with farmers, as it offered both power and economy. In fact by 1960, after the arrival of the Power Major, almost 90 per cent of Majors sold were diesel-powered.

Despite being radically different to its predecessor, Fordson's engineers strove to cut costs wherever possible and so if old parts or tooling could be used, they were. This was the case with the gearbox, as the E27N's was adopted and changed slightly to include a dual-range shift – doubling the speeds previously offered by the old tractor.

The business-end of the tractor was all new, with a new hydraulic and three-point linkage design bringing the Major up-to-date. While they were at it, the designers at Fordson also came up with a new one-piece drawbar.

In a bid to freshen-up the dated E27N, Fordson kicked the dark blue livery into touch, opting to adorn the new, curvier panels in Empire Blue – a lighter shade that better complemented the orange

A Power Major-based County Full Track ploughing on the land. Photo: Peter D Simpson

Technical specification

Produced:	1952-1958
Engine:	Ford E1ADDN (diesel)
Cylinders:	4
Bore x stroke:	3.74in x 4.52in
Displacement:	220cu in
Torque:	Diesel: 162lb ft @1,200rpm
Horsepower:	Diesel: 40.5hp
	Petrol: 38.5hp
	TVO: 39.5hp
Transmission:	6 forward, 2 reverse
Speed range:	2.0mph – 16.2mph
Linkage:	Category II
Lift capacity:	2,315lbs
Weight:	4,570lbs
Tyre sizes:	Front: 6.00x16 or 7.50x16
	Rear: 12.4x36 or 14x30

The new Major E1A was much more pleasing to the eye than its austere predecssor. Photo: Peter D Simpson

wheels. Farmers instantly liked the new look and bought the tractor in their droves.

The year 1957 heralded the arrival of two changes to the Major; an engine upgrade and the option of Live Drive. The Mk II engine was now under the bonnet, pushing out 44hp and the tvo option was phased out.

The Power Major arrived a year later with its 51hp Mk III engine, improved transmission and three-spoke front wheels.

In 1960 the Super Major appeared with the same engine, but the transmission was further improved with a diff-lock and the hydraulics were now named Qualitrol – featuring automatic depth control and position control. Disc brakes were fitted too, but the most obvious change was the repositioning of the headlights from the side of the bonnet to within the grille.

A blue and grey livery was the order of the day with the birth of the New Performance Super Major in 1963, along with an engine upgrade to 55hp and the change from cast to the pressed steel variety.

As was the case with its predecessor, the E1A proved popular for conversions. County created Full Track and high-clearance variants, while Kent Ford Dealers (KFD) created a narrow version for work on hop farms and in orchards. Lest we forget, the E1A was also the tractor that spawned the legendary Doe Dual-Drive.

The first incarnation of the Triple-D was, of course, the brainchild of Essex farmer George Pryor – who needed a more powerful tractor for ploughing his heavy clay land. Pryor believed that crawlers were unsuitable for the type of work he undertook on the farm and, unable to find anything else on the market that met his needs, set about building his own tractor from two E1As.

He devised the turntable system and rudimentary controls before his local Fordson dealer, Ernest Doe, became involved in the project and set about creating one of the most awe-inspiring tractors of the classic era.

Doe's Dual-Drive tractor arrived with the Power Major in 1958 (and was called the Dual Power), but would go on to see upgrades with the arrival of the Super Major (1960) and the New Performance Super Major (1963). Just six of the early models were built, as the tractor was deemed to be two vehicles by the Motor Taxation Department. ➡

A selection of large implements, produced by Doe, helped the machine to fulfil its potential – with an eight-furrow semi-mounted plough being the epitome of the range

Farmers were naturally reluctant to pay double for one machine and sales suffered as a result. The solution to this problem was to fit all of the hydraulic and auxiliary controls on the rear portion of the tractor. This also satisfied Health and Safety executives, who were unhappy that the operator had to select gears manually on the front unit before boarding at the back and setting off.

This was rectified in 1959 with an upgraded version of the tractor – now called the Doe Dual-Drive. Hydraulic slave cylinders now did most of the work changing gears and the power steering was driven by a pump attached to the crankshaft of the rear unit. An assistor ram was fitted to the three-point linkage and the famous blue with orange bonnet livery made its first appearance.

The Triple-D really came into its own with the introduction of the New Performance Super Major in 1963. As well as the operator now having the ability to control all of the gears from the rear unit, introduced with the arrival of the Super Major in 1960, diff-locks on both units gave true four-wheel drive – a real coup for Doe. The tractor could now pull bigger implements whilst still being able to turn on a sixpence at the headland.

The Doe Dual Drive wasn't all a bed of roses. The most obvious drawback was the scale of the tractor – a five-ton beast that was 20 feet long, without an implement

A Super Major-based Triple-D in full flow with Doe tool carrier and Doe four-furrow reversible plough. Photo: Peter D Simpson

in tow! Put a semi-mounted plough on the back and the whole ensemble was colossal. Throw an inexperienced operator into the mix and carnage ensued! Imagine approaching a junction with a whole tractor sticking out in front of you – edging out was an act of blind faith that relied on other road users having their wits about them. Steering at speed could also be a little daunting, with constant correction required to keep the machine on the straight and narrow.

A selection of large implements, produced by Doe, helped the machine to fulfil its potential – with an eight-furrow semi-mounted plough being the epitome of the range. Of course, production of more compact four-wheel drive tractors by Roadless, County and eventually Ford itself brought about the demise of the Triple-D – but by this time the tractor and the name Ernest Doe had achieved iconic status in the agricultural community.

As fate would have it, the E1A series was the last in a long line of tractors to have the Fordson badge adorning its bonnet. From now on, the all-new 6X series would bear the Ford name and would be produced at Basildon, rather than Dagenham. Many were worried that this was a mistake, but soon realised that the new Worldwide Series of tractors would build on the success enjoyed by the Major to become one the most well-liked range of tractors ever built in Britain. ∎

David Brown 50D

Meltham Mills, UK: 1953-1959

The 50D is a typical example of a tractor that is more popular now than it was when it was built. This is not to say that it wasn't a good tractor in its day – it was. With its enormous six-cylinder diesel engine and purpose-designed back end, the 50D was a true lugging machine that had the grunt to cope with the heaviest of loads.

As was the case with the early David Brown machines, the tractor was named in a way that described its features – the Vehicle Agricultural Diesel six-cylinder, or VAD6, but was actually badged as the 50D. It was also the first David Brown tractor to be offered solely with a diesel engine, which it shared with its tracked sister – the 50TD.

The tractor proved to be an immense puller, particularly good with cultivators, but was let down by the fact that it had no three-point linkage. This was of no real concern to David Brown though, as the company had envisaged that the tractor would be exported all over the world to be used as a towing machine – and wouldn't necessarily be a prime mover on the home market.

With 50hp and good torque on tap, the 50D was ideal for pulling trailers laden with sugar cane in plantations, across South Africa for example, whilst having a useful two-speed belt pulley for driving stationary machinery. The only problem was that threshing machines and other machines of this nature were becoming less common, due to the advent of the combine

The pride of any DB enthusiast's fleet, if he is lucky enough to have one, is a 50D. Photo: Kim Jackson

harvester and the increasing popularity of mains electricity within farm buildings.

In essence, the 50D was all about primitive power which is essentially the reason why it was so popular overseas. It had no hydraulics whatsoever and was just a simple machine that was easy to operate and maintain – perfect for large-scale operations in big countries – but not so good for British farmers.

It had several novel features including a sliding rear axle, four-speed pto and the inimitable David Brown bench seat. Perhaps its most striking features

Technical specification

Produced:	1953-1959
Engine:	David Brown
Cylinders:	6
Bore x stroke:	3.625in x 4in
Displacement:	248cu in
Torque:	Unknown
Horsepower:	50hp
Transmission:	6 forward, 2 reverse
Speed range:	1.51mph – 12.8mph
Linkage:	Drawbar only
Lift capacity:	N/A
Weight:	6,130lbs
Tyre sizes:	Front: 7.50x18
	Rear: 14x30

The tractor proved to be an immense puller, particularly good with cultivators, but was let down by the fact that it had no three-point linkage

are the louvred engine covers and the headlights – positioned level with the top of the bonnet, to remain clear of the belt during pulley operations.

In many ways, the 50D's only real competition was the Marshall MP6, which itself was more popular on the overseas market than it was at home. The 50D was 20hp down on the Marshall but still had what it took to be an excellent drawbar tractor and a worthwhile asset to David Brown's already-strong product line-up.

Today their scarcity, particularly on the British market, makes them highly sought-after machines, with examples that do come up for sale regularly reaching the £30,000 mark. Tractors originally registered in Britain tend to command more of a premium, but with only 1,260 produced all told, any 50D is a much-prized addition to any collection – whether solely David Brown or otherwise. ■

Believe it or not, Robin and Jackie McCaughey's Ford Golden Jubilee was bought in Northern Ireland in poor condition as a non-runner! Photo: Peter D Simpson

Ford NAA/ Golden Jubilee

Dearborn, Michigan, USA: 1953-1954

Most tractor enthusiasts, no matter on which side of the Atlantic they are, will be familiar with Ford's popular 8N. Those that reside in Britain, however, might not be aware of the Golden Jubilee Model – the 8N's replacement. This tractor was almost four years in the making and one glance will tell you that it is quite different to its predecessor.

Despite needing a fresh-faced machine to replace its outgoing model, Ford was keen to mark its 50th anniversary with a tractor that incorporated innovative new features – not simply a spruced-up version of the 8N. Nowadays, tractor manufacturers are renowned for using different colour schemes and extra gizmos to mark a special occasion, but the Golden Jubilee Model really was a new tractor.

Styling is the obvious thing to note – although the livery may have been retained, the bonnet was certainly very different. A bulbous nose replaced the swept-back look of the 8N, along with a more prominent ridge running the length of the bonnet that culminated in a curved panel that housed the tractormeter. The vertical bars of the 8N's radiator grille remained, but were capped by a more prominent round badge – a wheat stalk emblem that was similar to those that appeared on the British Fordson tractors. The distinctive radiator cap of the 8N was downgraded to a standard version that was now beneath the streamlined bonnet – that improved both aesthetics and visibility.

Underneath the bonnet was arguably the tractor's best feature – the engine. The 8N and other models used the flat head, side-valve Model A engine, but Ford was anxious that the Golden Jubilee Model should be different. Its engineers had worked hard to produce an engine that could be used for different applications and the result was the Red Tiger – a four-cylinder, overhead-valve unit that produced a useful 30hp. It had a shorter stroke than the side-valve motor, but a larger 3.44in bore that increased the displacement from 119.7cu in to 134 cu in.

At the back there were changes too. Gone was the pto-driven hydraulic pump that had its origins in the Ferguson system, being replaced by an engine-mounted pump – creating a live system that meant that the

Technical specification

Produced:	1953-1954
Engine:	Ford Red Tiger
Cylinders:	4
Bore x stroke:	3.4375in x 3.6in
Displacement:	134cu in
Torque:	198lb ft @1,125rpm
Horsepower:	30hp
Transmission:	4 forward, 1 reverse
Speed range:	2.68mph – 13.2mph
Linkage:	Category I
Lift capacity:	Unknown
Weight:	2,814lbs
Tyre sizes:	Front: 5.50x16
	Rear: 10x28

The tractor featured draft and position control as well as an engine-mounted hydraulic pump. Photo: Peter D Simpson

three-point linkage could be operated even when the clutch was depressed. The reasons for this change were two-fold; partly due to the infamous settlement between the Ford Motor Company and Harry Ferguson, but also to reflect continued research and development. Position and draft control were available to the operator and a small number of tractors were equipped with a live pto – an option on all models, but one rarely specified by cash-conscious farmers.

The Golden Jubilee Model looked similar in size to the 8N, but was actually 4 inches higher to accommodate the new engine and 4 inches longer to improve stability. The Red Tiger engine, amongst other refinements, also made the tractor fractionally heavier than the 8N, but this was barely noticeable.

Despite being aimed squarely at the American market, some Golden Jubilee Models and NAAs were sold in the Republic of Ireland but, as is the current trend, significant numbers have been imported by British and Irish enthusiasts in recent years. It is thought that the United States Air Force shipped some tractors over for use on airfields in England, but exact numbers are unknown.

It is also interesting to note that the Golden Jubilee Model was only designated as such in 1953. Tractors built in the following year, although they may look the same, were actually designated as NAA models by Ford. They can be easily identified by the different bonnet emblem, as 12 stars replaced the anniversary commemoration on the outer edge of the earlier tractors' insignias.

The Golden Jubilee Model tractors were popular with farmers, with over 77,000 built in 1953 and a further 50,000+ NAAs built in the following year. They were machines that had all the hallmarks of a good tractor – a decent engine, useful transmission and capable hydraulics, coupled with an attractive styling and livery package. The 600 series replaced the two designations in the latter half of 1954, but many of the Golden Jubilee Model and NAA's features were retained – testament to the excellent original design. ∎

> A bulbous nose replaced the swept-back look of the 8N, along with a more prominent ridge running the length of the bonnet

The Golden Jubilee featured a different bonnet style to the 8N. Photo: Peter D Simpson

This BTD-6 has a hydraulic oil tank and spool valve fitted for operating a remote cylinder. Photo: Gina Harvey

McCormick IH BTD-6

Doncaster, UK: 1953-1975

sk anyone to name a great crawler and a few models will keep cropping up; the Track-Marshall 55 and 75, County Full Track and the International Harvester BTD-6. Just what made the BTD-6 the farmers' favourite is hard to say; perhaps it was the machine's simplicity, or maybe its reliability? But it's fair to say that the BTD-6 was held in high regard by operators – becoming a true legend amongst agricultural machinery.

As with many other designs of the period, the engine played a significant role in the machine's character and capability.

The indirect injection, 40hp BD-264 engine used in the crawler was a slow-revving unit and was perfect for the BTD-6 – producing torque by the bucket load whilst being light, reliable and simple to maintain. Early American-built T-6 crawlers used a heavier and thirstier petrol engine and so the Doncaster-built BTD-6 was seen as a step forward in crawler design.

During the crawler's production run over 20,000 were built in various guises, with numerous optional extras, proving that the BTD-6 was well-liked by farmers and the construction industry alike. As popular as the standard agricultural spec model was, you are as likely to come across the famous 'Drott' examples when

A BTD-6, with five bottom track rollers, at work in Lincolnshire. Photo: Peter D Simpson

looking for a BTD-6. Large numbers of the machine were manufactured with dozer blades, but in the construction industry it was the diminutive four-in-one bucket

The famous logo adorning the side of the operator's platform. Photo: Julian Cooksley

The headlights are almost as iconic as the crawler. Photo: Julian Cooksley

The BD-264 engine used a CAV in-line fuel pump. Photo: Julian Cooksley

During the crawler's production run over 20,000 were built in various guises...

that was held in the highest esteem by owners – a true jack of all trades.

When it started life in 1953, the BTD-6 was equipped with a 40hp version of the engine used in the Farmall BMD and International Harvester BWD-6 tractors but, in 1955 another 10hp would be squeezed out of the well-liked powerplant. Other significant changes to the specification over the years included five bottom track rollers, front weight pack, work lights, pto, key starting and, on later models, a three-point linkage – as optional extras.

By the time production of the BTD-6 had ceased in 1975, no other British manufacturer had produced more crawlers, but as we all know – units produced isn't necessarily equal to popularity. IH worked hard to build on the initial success enjoyed by the BTD-6 and, in a bid to

take a stranglehold on the market, even produced an economy version – the BTD-640 – to cater for farmers on a budget and for those that simply didn't require all of the bells and whistles. The BTD-640 was essentially a de-rated version of the BTD-6 with simpler track rollers, minus their guards, and without a front weight and lights.

Cabs were never offered by International Harvester, but were later produced by Lambourn and Suntrac. Neither was particularly operator-friendly with the Lambourn being flimsy and the Suntrac noisy, but both provided welcome relief from the elements in winter.

There appears to be no magic formula that made the BTD-6 the farmers' favourite, it just seems to have been the right machine at the right time and, more importantly, the right price. ∎

Technical specification

Produced:	1953-1975
Engine:	IH BD-264
Cylinders:	4
Bore x stroke:	4in x 5.25in
Displacement:	264cu in
Torque:	200lb ft @1,100rpm
Horsepower:	40hp
	Later models uprated to 50hp
Transmission:	5 forward, 1 reverse
Speed range:	1.5mph – 5.4mph
Linkage:	Optional
Lift capacity:	Unknown
Weight:	9,100lbs
Track sizes:	14in or 16in

For some reason, the Hunting Pink and Light French Blue colour scheme was not well-liked compared to other David Brown liveries. Photo: Peter D Simpson

David Brown 900

Meltham Mills, UK: 1956-1958

In 1956, David Brown was buzzing. Having completed the acquisition of Harrison, McGregor and Guest Ltd the previous year, DB was now able to offer an expanded range of farm implements that would complement its tractors. It was hoped that the brilliant Albion range of machinery, now in David Brown colours, would help the company to win over farmers who had allegiances to other brands – but as we all know, it's never that simple!

Although successful and popular with those that had bought them, David Brown tractors were very often disregarded by potential buyers as they deemed them to be underpowered. The company's method of model designation led farmers to believe, for example, that the 25 model produced 25hp when it was actually 30hp. The 1956 launch of the 900 put paid to this confusion.

The 900 instantly attracted attention, as farmers could relate to the familiar off-set driving position and Hunting Pink (albeit with Light French Blue wheels) livery, whilst having the choice of four powerplants; petrol/tvo, petrol, diesel, or high-compression petrol – ranging from 37hp to 45hp. The diesel was the most popular choice and heralded the introduction of the now-popular CAV distributor-type injection pump – a real trendsetter at the time.

3-forward, 1-reverse transmission with two ranges and was controlled by either a standard foot pedal or an independent hand lever located on the left-hand mudguard – a somewhat quirky set-up, but one that was essential to the way the tractor functioned. The final drive was through spiral bevel gears and differential to a spur reduction at each wheel.

At the rear, the three-point linkage had lift, hold and lower functions and was both category I and II – all useful features. It emphasised the tractor's capability to operate increasingly larger implements, up to 1,800lbs in weight, whilst enabling farmers to utilise implements they had bought in previous years. The linkage had a unique safety feature that comprised a spring-adjusted device that released the hand clutch when the implement encountered an obstacle. Four types of drawbar were also available; a fixed plate was standard, but a swinging type, rectangular frame type and new-style pick-up hitch were all optional.

The introduction of Live-Drive in 1957 won over a few more of the 900's critics. This dual-clutched machine gave farmers a live power take-off and live hydraulics – a first for a David Brown tractor. Also during the revamp of the model, the steering column was moved to a central position, the front badge was now of a horizontal design and the engine frame was now fully enclosed.

Almost 14,000 machines were built before the new 950 model was launched,

Technical specification

Produced:	1956-1958
Engine:	David Brown
Cylinders:	4
Bore x stroke:	3.625in x 4in
Displacement:	165cu in
Torque:	105lb ft @1,300rpm
Horsepower:	AD4/30H: 40hp
	AK4/30H: 37hp
	AG4/30H: 40hp
	PAG4/30H: 45hp
Transmission:	6 forward, 2 reverse
Speed range:	1.42mph – 15.2mph
Linkage:	Category I & II
Lift capacity:	1,800lbs
Weight:	4,000lbs
Tyre sizes:	Front: 6.00x16
	Rear: 11.25x28

proving the tractor's popularity. It had to be good, and was, as the Fordson Major was proving to be a real hit with the farming fraternity, and the arrival of a new, bigger tractor from Massey Ferguson was rumoured to be imminent. ∎

It had to be good, and was, as the Fordson Major was proving to be a real hit...

As with any great tractor though, success wasn't immediately guaranteed – as it was reported that there were teething problems with the fuel pump. When driven from the production line at Meltham the engines appeared to be fine, but after a few hours' work on the farm the pumps would fail. Extensive research revealed that, during transit, the crates containing the pumps were being dropped – leading to the eventual seizing of the units. This was easily rectified, but lasting damage was done to David Brown's reputation outside the company's loyal following.

The 900's engine channelled power through a 10in Borg & Beck clutch to a

The external oil bath air cleaner was somewhat untidy but did the same job as 'neater' systems. Photo: Peter D Simpson

A restored Marshall MP6 is always a joy to behold. Photo: Jonathan Whitlam

Marshall MP6

Gainsborough, UK: 1954-1961

The Marshall MP6 was a great tractor – when it was working. It's reasonable to say that it had its fair share of teething troubles, but was to emerge as a good pulling machine that was used across the globe in the agricultural, civil engineering and industrial sectors.

The 1954 design was essentially a re-engined MP4, after Marshall managed to secure the supply of large quantities of the Leyland UE350 six-cylinder diesel engine. This was a much-respected unit that had seen use in many commercial and industrial applications, including some Fowler crawlers.

The tractor was chiefly designed for the overseas market and the prairie regions of Australia, South Africa and such countries – hence the name Marshall Prairie 6 – although sales of the tractor occurred across the globe. Of the 197 machines produced, only 10 were sold in Britain and one in the Republic of Ireland – quite remarkable for a home-grown tractor of the period.

From the outset, the MP6 was besieged with final drive problems, mostly centring around the bull gears and their housings. The bull gear teeth were susceptible to heavy loadings and snapped off, resulting in cracked castings and a loss of transmission oil.

Marshall rectified the problem of weak castings by introducing webbed supports and replaced the spur-type gears with a helical-cut design, which improved matters radically. By this time, though, word had spread – and fast, as bad news generally does, tarnishing the MP6's reputation. This was unfortunate, as the tractor was generally liked by those who used one in anger – after the transmission modifications had been made.

It was certainly a striking machine – at 151in long and 67in to the top of the radiator – it had an imposing stance which was softened by its clean, flowing panels and sloping chassis channels. These aesthetics were enhanced further by a beautiful livery that put other manufacturers' two-tone paint schemes to shame. The striking Chrome Orange of the MP4 was retained for the panels and chassis, while the Field-Marshall's silver wheels gave the tractor an instantly-recognisable identity. This was intensified by the Duck Egg Blue Leyland engine that seemed to be almost framed by an interestingly-shaped aperture in the bonnet.

Technical specification

Produced:	1954-1961
Engine:	Leyland UE350
Cylinders:	6
Bore x stroke:	3.96in x 4.75in
Displacement:	350cu in
Torque:	Unknown
Horsepower:	70hp
Transmission:	6 forward, 2 reverse
Speed range:	1.71mph – 14.6mph
Linkage:	Drawbar only
Lift capacity:	N/A
Weight:	8,150lbs
Tyre sizes:	Front: 7.50x18
	Rear: 14x34

An MP6 in its working clothes at a West Country rally. Photo: Joseph Lewis

The MP6 falls into the unenviable category of rare breed, in that so few were built. Many were either scrapped or abandoned because of their final drive problems. This makes the remaining machines highly-prized items – particularly those that were originally supplied to British farmers. If one does appear at auction it generates a vast amount of interest, with feverish bidding from enthusiasts and 'money-makers' alike.

Of those that are already in the hands of collectors, it is unusual to find one working at an event as it is often considered too risky to put the machine under strain – particularly with transmission parts so difficult to obtain. If you are lucky enough to see an MP6 'in the metal' at a show, take the time to look over it as it is a machine that marked the end of the glory days of one of Great Britain's most well-respected agricultural machinery manufacturers. ◼

... was to emerge as a good pulling machine that was used across the globe in the agricultural, civil engineering and industrial sectors

It's rare to see an MP6 at work, as many owners consider them to be too precious. Photo: Paul Tofield

Tractor
& Machinery

- ▪ **Finds and discoveries**
- ▪ **Practical guides**
- ▪ **Buyer's guides**
- ▪ **Competitions**
- ▪ **Sales results**
- ▪ **Restorations**
- ▪ **Tractormart**

396 GPY

The world's best-selling tractor magazine

The compact 'Little Giant' featured live hydraulics and was priced at around £500. Photo: Scott Lambert

McCormick IH B-250

Bradford, UK: 1956-1961

Many tractors have claimed 'firsts' in years gone by, but the McCormick IH B-250 was a real trend-setter and could lay claim to two – as it was the first British tractor to have disc brakes and the first to have a differential lock. This was IH's attempt at taking some of the ground back from Ferguson who had stolen a march with the TE-20 and, latterly, the FE 35.

The British-designed and built 'Little Giant' – as it became known – was compact, had live hydraulics and was priced at around £500, all factors that enabled dealers to score a sale over the popular Ferguson. The diesel-powered, 30hp B-250 was the first tractor to be produced at the newly-acquired Jowett car factory in Bradford, a facility that would later become synonymous with small tractor production – with the highly-acclaimed B-275, B-414 and 434 all built there.

It was always intended that the Idle works would produce the small tractors, while the Wheatley Hall Road factory in Doncaster would concentrate on the larger models and component production. The system worked well and by the end of the first full year of production, the factory had produced just under 3,500 units. The production line and sales of the tractor were so successful that in excess of 30,000 B-250s were built. This was obviously nowhere near the half million TE-20s built at Banner Lane, but an impressive tally all the same. Some B-250s would eventually be built at the Carr Hill facility in Doncaster, but it is unclear just how many emerged from the factory.

The square bonnet assembly of the B-250 was very different to that of its bigger brother, the 55hp B-450, but both machines featured an identical grille and shell-type mudguards to the rear – providing a unified feel, despite the obvious size difference. It was, however, what lay behind the grille that was one of the best features of the B-250. ➡

… the IH's overall package was more than a match for the grey and gold machine, with the standard diff-lock a real coup

Gerry Bosworth chooses to use an IH B-12 plough with his B-250, rather than a Ransomes model. Photo: Scott Lambert

The BD-144 engine was a lively four-cylinder unit that was much-loved by operators because of its impressive stamina in tough conditions. With a rated speed of 1,750rpm, the little McCormick was never really under strain with all of the grunt coming from lower down the rev range – a feature of many IH-designed engines in the years that would follow. Again, like other IH motors, the BD-144 required plenty of heat to get it up-and-running – but once started you couldn't fail to be impressed by its smoothness and lugging ability.

Ferguson's Standard 23C-powered 35, despite having a reputation for poor starting, was strong competition for the B-250 – with an excellent hydraulic system and useful transmission – but the IH's overall package was more than a match for the grey and gold machine, with the standard diff-lock a real coup.

The Fordson Dexta was the B-250's other main competition, with many waxing lyrical about the three-cylinder engine's impressive characteristics. Those loyal to the IH brand were dubious about the

Dexta's capabilities as, like the FE 35, the Fordson weighed more than 400lbs less than the B-250. The Ferguson TE-20 had previously proved that weight wasn't the key to traction, but those used to McCormick tractors had grown accustomed to the inherent weight characteristics and felt that it was beneficial when undertaking heavy-draft operations. Over-engineering and built-in mass would continue to be a key feature of International Harvester's tractors, but it never really appeared to harm the reputation that the company enjoyed.

an uprated version of the BD-144 engine and a dual-range gearbox – worthy additions to an already-brilliant machine. The engine, like many other IH units, would find its way into machines built by IH and others – in both agricultural and industrial applications. It was heavily used in forklifts and swathing machines, but also found use in stand-by generators, compressors and the like.

Almost 30,000 B-250s were built in Bradford – although nowhere near the number of Ferguson TE-20s produced, it is an impressive tally all the same. Due to their excellent build quality and reliability, many still exist and have found their way into preservation. They are popular tractors at ploughing matches where, married to an IH B-12 mounted plough with ACE bodies, they can prove to be a formidable combination. Other B-250s are still hard at work on farms providing sterling service with loaders and the venerable B-23 mower, where their dexterity, lively engine and never-say-die attitude still makes them firm favourites today. ∎

Technical specification	
Produced:	1956-1961
Engine:	IH BD-144
Cylinders:	4
Bore x stroke:	3.37in x 4in
Displacement:	144cu in
Torque:	109.9lb ft @1,300rpm
Horsepower:	30hp
Transmission:	5 forward, 1 reverse
Speed range:	1.68mph – 13.67mph
Linkage:	Category I
Lift capacity:	2,271lbs
Weight:	3,417lbs
Tyre sizes:	Front: 5.50x15
	Rear: 11x28

The B-250 was produced in cab-less configuration with shell-type mudguards, but many were, as was the trend, retro-fitted with Lambourn or Sta-Dri units. These were obviously primitive compared to later safety cabs, but provided solace during inclement weather. An industrial version of the tractor was produced that featured full mudguards and these are now highly prized by avid collectors.

Two years before the end of production of the B-250, the B-275 was introduced. This was heavily-based on the B-250, but featured

Ken Lloyd aboard his B-250 which is one of the earliest restored examples being 25th off the production line. Photo: Howard Sherren

A 1961 Fordson Dexta restored by Paul and Laura Shaw. Photo: Gina Harvey

Fordson Dexta/ Super Dexta

Dagenham, UK: 1958-1964

Technical specification

Produced:	1958-1964
Engine:	Ford F3.144
	Ford F3.152
Cylinders:	3
Bore x stroke:	3.5in x 5in
	3.6in x 5in
Displacement:	144cu in
	152cu in
Torque:	92lb ft @1,200rpm
	112lb ft @1,250rpm
Horsepower:	32hp
	44.5hp
Transmission:	6 forward, 2 reverse
Speed range:	1.7mph – 16.8mph
Linkage:	Category I
Lift capacity:	1,850lbs
Weight:	2,981lbs
Tyre sizes:	Front: 5.50x16
	Rear: 11x28

The Dexta is to Ford and Fordson fans what the 35 or 135 is to Massey Ferguson followers – *the* little British tractor. It has to be said that they were remarkably similar in many ways: a three-cylinder Perkins diesel engine at the front, six-speed transmission in the middle and at the back, a three-point linkage with position and draft control.

This is largely due to the fact that the makes came from the same lineage, but were subtly different due to patent restrictions. The MF 35, as most readers will know, was derived from the iconic Ferguson TE-20 – and the Dexta was essentially an adapted Ford 8N, which had many Ferguson traits.

Ford had been experimenting with light tractors for many years before it finally decided that developing the 8N was the easiest way forward. A Perkins P3 was originally fitted for evaluation purposes, but Ford was keen to build engines in-house to save money. It eventually transpired, after much collaboration with Perkins, that Ford would build a new foundry at Dagenham to produce the main engine components, whilst Perkins would assemble the new Dexta engine at its Peterborough facility. The new, 32hp powerplant was known as the F3.

One of the main concerns in developing the new tractor was ensuring that Ferguson's patents, of which there were in excess of 100, were not infringed. This meant that changes had to be made to the hydraulic system, among other things, but this didn't affect the Dexta's ability to perform well with mounted implements.

The tractor was launched to the trade and Press at a week-long event at Alexandra Palace, London, in November 1957. Alongside the tractor was a range of implements, developed jointly between Ransomes of Ipswich and Ford, that were designed specifically for use with the Dexta. Incidentally, at the end of the tractor's development, the machine was designated the 957E, but was launched as the Dexta. There is no definitive reason why the tractor was named this way, with some believing that it was derived from the word 'dextrous', itself stemming from the word 'dexterity' meaning 'skill in handling'. Others are adamant that it originated from Dexter cattle; a hardy Irish breed famed for its compact stature.

Whatever the origins of its name, the £555 Dexta was an immediate success story for Ford – propelling the company to market-leader status. From the beginning of mass-production in February 1958 to the end of the year, over 20,000 Dextas were built alongside over 35,000 Majors – helping the company to regain its position as Britain's largest manufacturer of agricultural tractors.

Production of the tractor had been underway for almost three years when an improved version was introduced to Europe at Ford's Hamburg convention. An improved transmission and better hydraulics were now incorporated, along with a re-styled grille assembly. Contrary to popular belief, headlights integrated into the radiator grilles were introduced while the Dexta was still in production and not when the Super Dexta was launched in 1962. A diff-lock was also introduced as standard equipment to the Dexta less than a year before the Super Dexta's launch at the Smithfield Show.

The arrival of the Super Dexta didn't spell the end of its predecessor, as the old model remained in production alongside the new tractor, albeit with the same mechanically-governed Simms Minimec fuel pump that graced the new engine. The new Super 3 engine, as it was known,

A single-furrow, deep-digger plough was well within the capacity of the New Performance Super Dexta. Photo: Peter D Simpson

was a 152cu in version of the original, that developed 39.5hp – a useful improvement over the old motor. The Super Dexta evolved into the 44.5hp New Performance Super Dexta in 1963 – featuring a new grey and blue livery – but was only in production for just over a year as the space occupied by the manufacturing facility was required for a new engine plant.

There's no doubt that the Fordson Dexta was a great achievement as it was reliable and affordable – whilst helping Ford to retain its position as one of the biggest tractor manufacturers. It proved to be a viable alternative to both the Ferguson FE 35 and Massey Ferguson 35 – tractors that would have otherwise exerted a stranglehold on the market. ∎

The Roadless Dexta was introduced at the 1959 Smithfield Show. The tractor shown here is a Roadless Super Dexta that would have cost just over £1,100 in 1962. Photo: Peter D Simpson

John Sharpe's MF 35 has won many awards, including Best Concours Tractor at Tractor World in 2005. Photo: Julian Cooksley

Massey Ferguson 35/X

Coventry, UK: 1958-1964

Many people say the Massey Ferguson 135 was the best tractor the company ever made, but the 35 certainly gave it a run for its money. The 135 was obviously part of MF's new unified range of tractors, but having a bigger brother with identical controls, in the shape of the 65, the 35 was a brilliant little package from the Coventry-based concern.

The grey and gold FE 35 was a good stepping-stone towards what would become an immensely popular tractor – but the jury was still out on the Standard 23C diesel engine. Petrol, tvo and lamp oil-powered versions of the 35 were available to farmers, but the diesel version was by far the

most popular. The best thing the Standard unit had going for it was that it was a known quantity in that everyone knew what it was capable of and what to expect from it.

The 35's popularity really took off in 1959 when the Perkins A3.152 engine was introduced. In many people's eyes, the 35 was now the tractor it was supposed to be – retaining the compact nature and design ethic of the legendary TE-20, whilst having a gutsy powerhouse up front. One of the best features of the new engine was that it actually started like an engine should – no drama or fuss, just instant reaction at the turn of the key!

Once farmers realised that the 35 was now a completely different animal, they bought it in droves. That distinctive rasping chatter from the exhaust was

heard on farms the length and breadth of Britain, with the Perkins-powered tractor receiving critical acclaim wherever it was put to work. Of course, the beauty of MF's design and infrastructure meant that all bases had been covered and the tractor could be rolled out in guises that would suit every situation and budget – vineyard, agricultural and industrial.

The 35's dash panel was simple and all controls fell easily to hand. Photo: Julian Cooksley

The power and torque generated by the three-cylinder unit made the 35 a pleasure to operate in the field, particularly in high-draft operations. Admittedly, it wasn't as smooth as the outgoing Standard 23C but it had a character and resonance that could make the driver smile. Coupled with MF's extensive range of implements, the 35 certainly was the ideal tool for the job – ideal for ploughing with a three-furrow, or even four-furrow, conventional plough in the right conditions – but equally at home mowing hay where its agility made it the perfect choice for livestock farmers.

Features that appealed to farmers were the excellent Ferguson hydraulic system with automatic two-way draft control, dual clutch with live-drive and a well-spaced range of gears for both field and road work.

The addition of a differential lock in 1962 brought the tractor up-to-scratch, before the arrival of the ultimate 35 – the 35X.

The A3.152X-powered 35X was the crème de la crème of small tractors, with a host of features that set it apart from the competition. A high-specification 35X was at the top of many farmers' wish-lists – with all of the bells and whistles it really was a stunning tractor. The now highly-prized Multi-Power transmission, PAVT rear wheels, swinging drawbar and foot throttle were all options that turned a great tractor into a fantastic tractor – a real gem.

The 35 was such a success that variants of it were built not only in Britain, but also in France and the United States – albeit with different names. In fact, the 35 was such a good tractor that it continues to be built under licence in India by Tractors and Farm Equipment, TAFE, with Perkins-style engines and similar styling to the original. The Yugoslavian-produced IMT 539 was also of a similar nature, but was available with IMT's own styling. ■

The 35's popularity really took off in 1959 when the Perkins A3.152 engine was introduced

A fully-restored MF 35 is always a joy to behold. Photo: Julian Cooksley

Technical specification

Produced:	1958-1964
Engine:	Standard petrol, tvo, lamp oil & diesel
	Perkins A3.152 diesel
	Perkins A3.152X diesel (35X only)
Cylinders:	Standard: 4
	Perkins: 3
Bore x stroke:	Standard petrol, tvo & lamp oil: 3.425in x 3.622in
	Standard 23C diesel: 3.312in x 4in
	Perkins: 3.6in x 5in
Displacement:	Standard petrol, tvo & Standard lamp oil: 133.4cu in
	Standard 23C diesel: 137.8cu in
	Perkins: 152.6cu in
Torque:	Std petrol: Unknown
	Std tvo: Unknown
	Std lamp oil: Unknown
	Std 23C diesel: 108.4lb ft @1,700rpm
	Perkins A3.152: 110.6lb ft @1,250rpm
	Perkins A3.152X: 119lb ft @1,300rpm
Horsepower:	Std petrol: 37hp
	Std tvo: 30hp
	Std lamp oil: 29hp
	Std 23C diesel: 37hp
	Pekins A3.152: 37hp
	Perkins A3.152X: 44.5hp
Transmission:	6 forward, 2 reverse
Speed range:	0.32mph – 14mph
Linkage:	Category I
Lift capacity:	2,500lbs
Weight:	Standard petrol, tvo & lamp oil: 2,940lbs
	Standard 23C diesel: 3,150lbs
	Perkins: 3,185lbs
Tyre sizes:	Front: 4.00x19 or 6.00x16
	Rear: 10x28 or 11x28

The list of standard equipment on the 65 was quite spectacular, with the excellent Ferguson system, dual clutch, disc brakes and dual-category linkage

Massey Ferguson 65

Coventry, UK: 1958-1964

The Massey Ferguson 65 was the 35 for the large acreage farmer – a tractor built for big fields and arduous conditions. It benefited from all the features of its smaller sibling while having the power and torque that a larger, four-cylinder engine could provide.

After toying with the LTX prototype (essentially a TE-20 on steroids), it was decided this would prove too costly to put into production and so, in true make-do-and-mend style, the MF 35's transmission was mated to a larger engine, while the tin work and front axle were pure Ferguson 40. The 40 was an American-built model out of production by then, which meant that the redundant tooling

could be sent to Britain and put to good use. The new tractor was built with the sole intention of taking the fight to the likes of Nuffield and Ford in the 50hp sector.

Massey Ferguson had always intended that its tractors would be suitable for any operator – if you could drive one, then you could drive another; their identical controls made them perfect partners on a one-marque farm. Although not identical in appearance, the tractors' shell-type mudguards, sculpted bonnets and matching livery provided a unified look.

At the heart of the 65 was a Perkins four-cylinder unit developing just over 50hp – aiming the tractor squarely at those wishing to use either a four or five-furrow mounted plough. As well as the traditional conventional ploughs, MF was now able to demonstrate the 65 with the new model 85 three-furrow reversible.

The 65's rear wheel rims are very distinctive and quite different to those used by other tractor manufacturers. Photo: Bob Weir

Tom French, of Ayrshire, spent many hours restoring his Massey Ferguson 65 MkI. Photo: Bob Weir

With a fully-automatic tripping mechanism and spring-loaded breakaway beams, the 85 was the perfect match for the 65 – particularly as it weighed 1,500lbs – a substantial load for any tractor.

The 65 really was a big tractor for its day – with many potential buyers questioning if they actually needed a tractor that large. After all, for those that had been used to the benefits of a 37hp MF 35, a tractor with 13hp more was a big step up! The 65 naturally found favour on big farms and with contractors, where the features of such a machine could be utilised.

The list of standard equipment on the 65 was quite spectacular, with the excellent Ferguson system, dual clutch, disc brakes and dual-category linkage. In addition to these features, power steering, differential lock and heavy-duty hydraulic pump were available as options. Epicyclic reduction

was provided at the axle ends to enable higher transmission speeds to be reached and to improve braking efficiency.

Besides the standard agricultural model, a high-clearance version (offering 18¾in clearance) and two industrial models were available. Of these, the 65S was essentially a yellow and grey version of the agricultural model, with some other differences, while the 65R featured a Borg & Beck torque converter and shuttle transmission – which gave four forward and four reverse speeds – as its main selling point.

As was the case with the MF 35, the already-good 65 became great in 1960, when the MkII version was launched. This featured the direct-injection Perkins AD4.203 unit – with an 8hp increase over its predecessor, diff lock as standard and would, eventually, feature the renowned Multi-Power transmission on the list of options.

All-in-all, the 65 – in MkI and MkII forms – was one of the best tractors of its generation and proved so reliable that it

The 'triple triangle' that adorns the 65's bonnet. Photo: Bob Weir

would form the basis of the 165, with very few mechanical differences – the sign of a great machine. After all, as we well know, if it ain't broke – don't fix it! ■

Technical specification

Produced:	1958-1964
Engine:	Perkins A4.192
	Perkins AD4.203
Cylinders:	4
Bore x stroke:	A4.192: 3.5in x 5in
	AD4.203: 3.6in x 5in
Displacement:	A4.192: 192cu in
	AD4.203: 203.5cu in
Torque:	A4.192: 141.6lb ft @1,200rpm
	AD4.203: 169lb ft @1,300rpm
Horsepower:	A4.192: 50.5hp
	AD4.203: 58.3hp
Transmission:	6 forward, 2 reverse
	(doubled with Multi-Power on MkII)
Speed range:	0.5mph – 14.5mph
	(19mph top speed with Multi-Power)
Linkage:	Category I & II
Lift capacity:	2,500lbs
Weight:	4,158lbs
Tyre sizes:	Front: 6.00x16
	Rear: 11x32

An Allis-Chalmers ED-40 seen at a working event in the East Midlands. Photo: Paul Tofield

Allis-Chalmers ED-40

Essendine, UK: 1960-1968

The ED-40 among the top 50 tractors? Surely not! It's fair to say that the first version of the model wasn't the greatest tractor ever produced – but with important refinements throughout its production life, the ED-40 became a great little tractor.

It all began in Essendine, Lincolnshire, with A-C's realisation that it needed to replace its ailing D-272 with a new model – it was also becoming important to produce a diesel-powered tractor, as petrol/tvo engines were no longer in vogue. The obvious choice for Allis-Chalmers was to use a Perkins powerplant, but Massey Ferguson's buy-out of the company meant that it was unable

to reach an agreement for an engine – and so an alternative had to be sought.

The eventual solution was the tried-and-tested Standard Ricardo 23C – an engine that had seen use in the Ferguson FE 35 and early Massey Ferguson 35 models. As many people know, this engine was labelled a poor starter, but was the only viable option for Allis-Chalmers as it needed a reliable unit in relatively large numbers. The 23C was the only engine to offer that. In truth it was the engine that gave the ED-40 a bad reputation, but this would be rectified on later tractors with the introduction of an improved version of the 23C.

The first thing that should be said about the ED-40 is that it was certainly a good-looking tractor. Allis-Chalmers' familiar

orange livery was complemented by off-white wheels and a striking stance – with a side profile similar in many ways to that of the Farmall A. The compact engine flowed into a narrow bell housing and slender transmission casing giving the ED-40 a very narrow, almost vineyard-like, appearance. When viewed from the side, the lack of side rails placed the emphasis solely on the tin work – a simple, yet elegant, bonnet and unique mudguards. The exhaust is also unique in that it is very short, with a small pipe emerging from a stubby silencer – it's instantly ED-40.

The operator was treated to a platform quite unlike any other tractor of a similar size. First off, it was quite high up – giving the driver a commanding view of the work he was undertaking – with a comfortable seat and well-laid-out instrumentation on a sloping dash panel beneath the steering column. The gear levers were perhaps the only oddity, emerging from under the seat – making it difficult, at first, to select the desired range and gear. The ED-40 also featured a hand clutch to the driver's right, which allowed him to sit with his legs to one side. This proved to be particularly advantageous when

Technical specification

Produced:	1960-1968
Engine:	Standard Ricardo 23C diesel
Cylinders:	4
Bore x stroke:	3.3125in x 4in
Displacement:	138cu in
Torque:	110.6lb ft @1,250rpm
Horsepower:	37hp
Transmission:	8 forward, 2 reverse
Speed range:	0.4mph – 16.4mph
Linkage:	Category I
Lift capacity:	2,500lbs
Weight:	3,584lbs
Tyre sizes:	Front: 6.00x16
	Rear: 11x28

A restored example of an early ED-40. Photo: Paul Tofield

the tractor was equipped with a mid-mounted hoe or similar implement.

Allis-Chalmers spent a great deal of time developing the hydraulics and three-point linkage – resulting in a live system that offered selective weight transfer and its own oil reserve. Admittedly, the hydraulics were never the strongest point of the first ED-40s, but they were never remembered as being a particularly negative aspect.

The second incarnation of the tractor was the ED-40 Depthomatic, which offered automatic draft control, top-link sensing, automatic weight transfer and automatic variable response. This was a much better system – particularly for draft work, such as ploughing, but never lived up entirely to expectations. The other radical improvement was the uprated 23C engine that received glow-plug starting and an additional three horsepower.

The main problem with the ED-40 was that it emerged at just the wrong time. The Massey Ferguson 35 had a strangle-hold on the market and was tough to beat, particularly as it featured an excellent engine. As fate would have it, the ED-40 was the last British-built Allis-Chalmers tractor – a sad end for Essendine – although tractor production did continue in America. With its smooth delivery of power, good operator platform, useful hydraulic capability and exceptional road speed, the ED-40 was an excellent all-round performer, but it never received the critical acclaim that it deserved. ∎

The Allis-Chalmers ED-40 has recently become a popular tractor on the rally circuit. Photo: Jonathan Whitlam

Neville Porter aboard his highly-original Case 830. Photo: Gary Connolly

Case 830

Racine, Wisconsin, USA: 1960-1969

After working hard to improve its tractors in the 1950s, Case was anxious to consolidate the position that its tractors enjoyed and was keen not to lose ground to the competition. The 30 Series became renowned for its potent diesel engines and useful transmissions.

Coupled with a choice of chassis options, the tractors established themselves as capable workhorses across America. In reality, the new tractors were very much like their forerunners, albeit with a smattering of marketing spin to make them appear all-new and exciting, but as Case was feeling the pinch there was little it could do to improve its tractors until later in the decade.

The first thing that strikes you about the

Racine-built 830 is its stature – in that it is somewhat disproportionate! It had an almost stretched look about it, with a long wheelbase and plenty of clearance – it had a definite presence. Much like the British-built International Harvester 634, the length of the bonnet gave the impression that a monster was lurking underneath – a 100hp straight-six perhaps? In reality, an in-house four-pot Powrcel motor provided the power for what was marketed in the States as a five-plow machine. There's no doubt that the 830 could pull a five-furrow plough without too much drama, but its appearance led you to believe that it was capable of much more.

Following a lofty climb up to his platform the operator enjoyed an elevated position, came under the 830's umbrella. The 831 was a row-crop variant with Vee-twin front wheels, while the 840 and 841 were petrol-powered versions of the afore mentioned tractors. The models were launched at a time when petrol was still considered to be a viable tractor fuel, due to its low cost, resulting in many manufacturers continuing to offer farmers a choice of powerplants.

The basic transmission was more than capable of any job a farmer could throw at it, but the optional Case-o-Matic gearbox brought the 830 in-line with the clutch-less shifting offered on other manufacturer's models. Essentially, this was the same transmission but with the addition of a torque converter – very much like MF's Multi-Power and IH's Speed Amplifier.

At the rear a three-point linkage was standard, although a large number of implements used in prairie-style operations were still of the large, trailed variety – meaning that the linkage was often redundant. Two remote valves of 13.6gpm were on-hand to provide the hydraulic dexterity needed to operate folding tillage equipment and depth control on trailed and semi-mounted ploughs. A twin-speed pto meant that all eventualities were catered for, while a belt pulley was optional.

The 830 was only available as a two-wheel drive model, although its power and traction meant that it was never really troubled, except in the most arduous of conditions. Power-assisted steering could be specified for those that spent numerous hours in the seat.

Technical specification

Produced:	1960-1969
Engine:	J.I. Case Powrcel
Cylinders:	4
Bore x stroke:	4.375in x 5in
Displacement:	301cu in
Torque:	Unknown
Horsepower:	64hp
Transmission:	8 forward, 2 reverse
	16 forward, 4 reverse (Case-o-Matic)
Speed range:	1.7mph – 17.6mph
Linkage:	Category II
Lift capacity:	Unknown
Weight:	7,175lbs
Tyre sizes:	Front: 6.00x16
	Rear: 13.6x38

The 30 Series and the $6,000 830 were eventually replaced in 1969 by the 70 Series – a range that would become a favourite of American farmers, with the Agri King name living on as a sign of quality and productivity. ∎

> A twin-speed pto meant that all eventualities were catered for, while a belt pulley was optional

with a commanding view all-round and an almost bird's-eye-perspective of the implement. While on the subject of the operator's platform, it should be said that the early models provided a significant perch for the driver, but later tractors were equipped with the 'Comfort King' system. This was a forerunner to later safety and acoustic developments, but essentially meant that the platform was mounted higher, on rubber dampers, away from the chassis to reduce noise and vibrations. This system was available from 1964 in both cabbed and cab-less guises, as pioneered on the six-cylinder 930 model.

Besides the standard tractor, three other models were available – although they all

A three-point linkage was standard, although rarely used in prairie operations. Photo: Gary Connolly

A David Brown 990 in the model's final livery of white and Case Power Red. Photo: Peter D Simpson

David Brown 990

Meltham Mills, UK: 1961-1980

f all the tractors that have been built, the David Brown 990 probably underwent the most cosmetic changes – first it was red and yellow, then white and brown and finally, it was white and orange. The changes occurred over a long time, proving that it was fundamentally a good tractor – one worth developing and retaining in the product line-up for as long as possible.

The first incarnation of the 990 could trace its roots back to both the 900 model

and the more recent 950. Improvements were made on each model to create the next, culminating in a longer, stronger, better-geared and better-powered tractor in the shape of the 990 Implematic. It was Hunting Pink (red) with yellow wheels, grille and silencer – a nice-looking machine that retained the styling of its predecessors with curved cut-outs on either side of the bonnet where the manifold was positioned.

Incidentally, the new tractor was the first to be produced at Meltham with a cross-flow cylinder head – which meant the inlet ports were on the opposite side

to the exhaust. Coupled with the fact that the air cleaner had been moved to the front of the tractor, allowing cooler air to enter the engine, the cross-flow head gave an increase in power – with 52hp being squeezed out of the four-cylinder unit.

The tractor used the company's patented David Brown Traction Control Unit for operating implements with depth wheels, but when using implements with no depth wheels, the top link acted on a Bowden cable that, in turn, worked a valve – thus hydraulically controlling implement depth.

David Brown launched the second version of the tractor in 1965 – the 990 Selectamatic – which was Chocolate Brown with Orchid White panels and wheels with a red silencer. Although the mudguards were retained from the Implematic, the bonnet assembly was different, having a square-cut appearance and red grille panels with a gold upper panel that housed the DB emblem.

Using the Selectamatic hydraulic system that had been pioneered on the 770 model, the 990 now had an added dimension. To the rear of the single-lever quadrant lay a dial-type arrangement that allowed the operator to switch between position control, draft control and external services – a novel, yet useful system. With this added hydraulic control and an extra 3hp from the engine, the 990 was a force to be reckoned with.

The final colour scheme adopted for the 990 followed the merger with Case. White panels were retained, but the Chocolate Brown was replaced by Case Power Red (orange) and the wheels were now the same colour as the skid unit. On the first tractors, the gold upper grille was kept but would later be white and house the headlights.

Significant improvements to the new 990, which had dropped the Selectamatic name, were the addition of a twelve-forward and four-reverse speed transmission, that had synchromesh on

eight of the forward gears, a twin-speed pto and another 3hp increase in power. Live-drive was achieved either through a two-stage pedal or hand-operated pto clutch. Perhaps the most notable though, was the option of four-wheel drive – a real coup for a tractor of this size.

A high-clearance option was available on two-wheel drive models that basically consisted of lengthened kingpins which could be fitted on the farm. The final-drive units on the rear axle were then turned through 90 degrees, giving an extra 7½in of ground clearance.

Other options included hydrostatic steering, wheel and front-end weights and the choice of shell-type mudguards or reinforced versions that could accept either the DB Weatherframe or a full cab. An industrial version was also available, with a choice of options that included front drum brakes, in a yellow-with-red-wheels livery.

As it would turn out, the 990, in all its forms, would be the second most popular

tractor turned out by the company, behind the inimitable Cropmaster. It might not have had the lively characteristics of the three-cylinder powered David Browns, but it had a good engine all the same and won over many farmers with its range of features – particularly in Selectamatic guise. ∎

... the David Brown 990 probably underwent the most cosmetic changes – first it was red and yellow, then white and brown and finally, it was white and orange

One of David Brown's best-selling tractors was the 990 Implematic. Photo: Kim Jackson

Technical specification

Produced:	1961-1980
Engine:	DB AD4/47
	DB AD4/49
	DB AD4/49001
Cylinders:	4
Bore x stroke:	DB AD4/47: 3.63in x 4.5in
	DB AD4/49: 3.94in x 4in
	DB AD4/49001: 3.94in x 4in
Displacement:	DB AD4/47: 185.8cu in
	DB AD4/49: 195cu in
	DB AD4/49001: 195cu in
Torque:	DB AD4/47: 154.2lb ft @1,200rpm
	DB AD4/49: 151.9lb ft @1,400rpm
	DB AD4/49001: 151.9lb ft @1,400rpm
Horsepower:	DB AD4/47: 52hp
	DB AD4/49: 55hp
	DB AD4/49001: 58hp
Transmission:	Implematic: 6 for., 2 rev.
	Selectamatic: 6 for., 2 rev./12 for., 4 rev.
	Synchromesh: 12 forward, 4 reverse
Speed range:	0.9mph – 16.6mph
Linkage:	Category I & II
Lift capacity:	Implematic: 3,307lbs
	Selectamatic: 4,255lbs
	Synchromesh: 4,255lbs
Weight:	Implematic: 4,905lbs
	Selectamatic: 5,401lbs
	Synchromesh: 5,754lbs
Tyre sizes:	Implematic: Front: 6.00x16
	Rear: 11x32
	Selectamatic: Front: 6.00x19
	Rear: 12.4x36
	Synchromesh: Front: 6.00x19
	Rear: 12.4x36

Nuffield 342

Cowley & Bathgate, UK: 1961-1964

The Nuffield 342, launched at the 1961 Smithfield Show, was one of the first tractors to be built at the ex-Morris factory at Cowley, near Oxford. It was, however, only produced there for less than two years – as the company moved to a purpose-built assembly plant in Bathgate, Scotland, which represented a company investment of more than £11 million.

Despite dropping the Universal name from the bonnet, the company decided to retain the five-forward, one-reverse transmission that had featured in the preceding Universal Three and DM series tractors. It was a good unit that offered a useful range of speeds, but was seen as a little archaic in comparison to the dual range gearboxes offered by the other manufacturers of the time. This would be rectified later with the introduction of the 10/42 model – essentially the same tractor, but now fitted

with an up-to-date transmission system that doubled the number of gears.

The 342 was aimed squarely at those who would otherwise buy a Massey Ferguson 35X or a Fordson Super Dexta and so it had to be good – very good. The Universal Three had proved popular with farmers and so uprating it with an extra 5hp could only be a good thing. Most liked the engine's characteristics but were disappointed by the tractor as a whole – it was deemed to be just too big.

It was said that Nuffield salesmen had asked for a tractor that could take on the might of the Fordson, MF and the McCormick IH B-250. And they got one – but not quite as they had hoped. It was a match for other tractors in terms of output and productivity, but wasn't particularly compact. Some farmers liked this, as the

Buyers were drawn to the 342 as it was sturdy, reliable and had a good pedigree – qualities that were required by thrifty farmers of the time. The very fact that it was reliable also made it the perfect export machine and many were sent overseas to work in far more harsh environments than would ever be experienced in Britain. The two main differences were the oversize tyres fitted to export machines and the taller air pre-cleaner pipe – applied to help keep the intake away from the dust experienced in many countries to which the tractor was exported.

As with the excellent Massey Ferguson 35 and 65, the Nuffield 342 and 460 represented a worthwhile pairing for any farmer that wanted to maintain a one-marque operation – particularly as the 57.5hp 460 was the most powerful British tractor available at the time. Although not the most advanced tractors of the period, they were based on proven technology, simple to maintain and were, on the whole, considered to be good value for money.

The Nuffield 342 is now popular with ploughmen and restorers as it is generally cheaper to buy than other tractors of a similar age, whilst having good parts availability and, with its striking Poppy Orange livery, it definitely cuts a dash on the rally circuit. ■

Technical specification

Produced:	1961-1964
Engine:	BMC OEG diesel
Cylinders:	3
Bore x stroke:	3.74in x 4.72in
Displacement:	171cu in
Torque:	118lb ft @1,600rpm
Horsepower:	42hp
Transmission:	5 forward, 1 reverse
Speed range:	0.8mph – 16.8mph
Linkage:	Category I & II
Lift capacity:	2,830lbs
Weight:	4,330lbs
Tyre sizes:	Front: 7.50x16
	Rear: 11x32

The 'tailored' green canvas seat cover complemented the Poppy Orange livery quite nicely. Photo: Jonathan Whitlam

A nicely-restored 342 will always attract attention. Photo: Jonathan Whitlam

extra 1,000lbs the Nuffield carried in relation to the MF 35X meant that traction was never really a problem – but, as we are aware, it's not all about brute force and ignorance.

A decent hydraulic system is key to the success of any tractor worth its fuel and, to be fair, the 342 had one – but it was never going to set the world alight when compared to the Ferguson System. Draft control via a single-acting top link system helped keep soil-engaging implements on the straight and narrow and a differential lock, as standard equipment, gave the tractor a fighting chance in arduous conditions. A two-furrow plough was the ideal implement for the tractor, but three-furrow ploughs could be pulled without too much difficulty if the soil type and weather conditions permitted.

... it is generally cheaper to buy than other tractors of a similar age, whilst having good parts availability and, with its striking Poppy Orange livery, it definitely cuts a dash on the rally circuit

Mark Symonds ploughing with his 1967 Zetor 3045 and IH B-12 plough. Photo: Joseph Lewis

The 3045 was a real coup for the Czechoslovakian company as it could compete with a Roadless Super Dexta or Roadless Ploughmaster 46 at a fraction of the cost. It was a purposeful-looking machine, with a centre-drive front axle and distinctive livery of gold chassis and bright red wheels and tin work. Although perhaps not as attractive as the 3545 (and 3511) that would replace it, the 3045 capitalised on the fact that it didn't look much different to an MF 35 – but with the added benefit

Zetor UR1 3011/3045

Brno, Czechoslovakia: 1962-1967

Zetor's new UR1 unified range of tractors, introduced in 1962, was a revelation. By using common components and a 'modular' engine system, the company was able to offer a complete range of tractors – starting at about £550 – whilst keeping manufacturing costs to a minimum. It also enabled Zetor to gain some ground on the more established British manufacturers, such as Massey Ferguson.

As with most middle-of-the-range tractors, the 3011 proved to be the most popular with European farmers – as its two-cylinder sibling was deemed too small and the four-cylinder 4011 was largely unnecessary, particularly when farmers felt that they were getting a bargain if they didn't buy the biggest model in the line-up. At £710, the full-specification 3011 was perfect for the thrifty farmer – a full £100 cheaper than the newly-released, base model MF 135.

The 3011 had been in production for three years when it was introduced into Britain by the Motor Imports Company, that later became Škoda (Great Britain) Ltd. It was something of an unknown quantity to British farmers, who were more

accustomed to the Massey Ferguson 35 and Fordson Dexta. The beauty of the tractor was that it offered an excellent specification at a budget price – just £650.

Like so many other manufacturers, Zetor was keen to offer models that would appeal to everyone and so introduced the 3013 narrow-track and 3016 half-track variants at the 1966 Smithfield Show, along with the 3045 four-wheel drive model. Although the 3016 was displayed at the show, it has been said that none were ever sold in Britain.

All models used the company's Z3001 diesel engine, with three cylinders and liquid cooling. Like so many other engines of a similar configuration, the 35hp Zetor unit was a punchy unit that seemed more powerful than it actually was – the perfect advertisement for Zetor. The Z3001 was also remarkably advanced for the time, as it incorporated a swirl chamber on top of the piston and a temperature-adjustable fuel pump that enabled the tractor to be operated in most climates.

When married to the ten-forward speed transmission, the tractor – regardless of configuration – was a worthy addition to any machinery shed. A dual clutch was standard – providing a live pto, along with the Zetormatic hydraulic system – featuring draft control.

Declan Robinson and his superbly-restored 3011. Photo: Peter D Simpson

of four-wheel drive. Farmers were naturally very sceptical of new machines, particularly those from far-flung places, so by using curved styling similar to tractors already established on the market, Zetor was able to appeal to the British farming community.

As well as having an excellent specification as standard, the 3011 and 3045 offered some very useful options. A passenger seat – as was all the rage on the Continent – was available, along with an air compressor and storage tank. This was ideal if you wanted to reduce the tyre pressures for ploughing and then inflate them again for road transport. A front-mounted pto was also available for the 3011, but could not be fitted to the 3045, as the four-wheel drive system utilised this shaft for drive.

All-in-all, the 3011 and 3045 were excellent tractors and the perfect machines for struggling and budget-conscious farmers but, unfortunately, would never have the impact and deserved success that the big-name brands would enjoy. ◼

Technical specification

Produced:	1962-1967
Engine:	Zetor Z3001
Cylinders:	3
Bore x stroke:	3.74in x 4.33in
Displacement:	142.8cu in
Torque:	94lb ft @1,400rpm
Horsepower:	35hp
Transmission:	10 forward, 2 reverse
Speed range:	0.68mph – 15.8mph
Linkage:	Category II
Lift capacity:	2,205lbs
Weight:	3011: 3,263lbs
	3045: 3,505lbs
Tyre sizes:	3011: Front: 6.00x16
	Rear: 12.4x28
	3045: Front: 8.00x20
	Rear: 12.4x28

… it became the most popular tractor of the era and one of the world's greatest classic tractors ever

The John Deere 4020 built between 1963 and 1972 was re-tested in 1969 giving an amazing 97hp at the pto. Just under 200,000 models were built of the 4020 which at the time made it Deere's most successful tractor. Photo: Peter D Simpson

John Deere 4020

Waterloo, Iowa, USA: 1963-1972

fter enjoying success with its legendary two-cylinder tractors, John Deere decided that all-fuel, multi-cylinder engines were the way to go and as a result, introduced the New Generation series of tractors in 1960. These were all four-cylinder machines with the exception of the range-topping 4010 – which had an in-house-designed six-cylinder unit beneath the bonnet.

These machines had been on the drawing board for seven years prior to their launch and were quite unlike anything seen before from JD. They were much sleeker and more elegant than the Johnny Poppers they replaced and had been designed with the operator in mind. They incorporated detailed instrumentation, ergonomic seating and a car-like steering column – truly the pinnacle of agricultural design.

The tractors were much-loved by farmers and admired by rival manufacturers who realised that the new tractors, particularly the 4010, were now the benchmark in tractor design. John Deere, of course, realised this but did not rest on its laurels and was quick to build on the

success enjoyed by the new models. It continually refined its designs, culminating in the launch of the 4020 in 1963.

The new tractor used some of its predecessor's components, including uprated versions of the petrol and diesel engines – LPG was consigned to the

Technical specification

Produced:	1963-1972
Engine:	John Deere 404
Cylinders:	6
Bore x stroke:	4.25in x 4.75in
Displacement:	404cu in
Torque:	260lb ft @ 1,100rpm
Horsepower:	106hp
Transmission:	8 forward, 2 reverse
	or 8 forward, 4 reverse
Speed range:	1.2mph – 20.5mph
Linkage:	Category II
Lift capacity:	3,790lbs
Weight:	8,510lbs
Tyre sizes:	Front: 7.50x18
	Rear: 18.4x34

history books, but its new transmission was the one thing that set it apart from the 4010. The dashboard-controlled, full-Powershift transmission was the first to offer clutchless changing under load with the convenience of one-lever operation. Eight forward and four reverse speeds enabled the operator to find a suitable gear for each job, whilst utilising the throttle and the engine's considerable torque output to give subtle variations in speed according to ground conditions. A foot-actuated differential lock also aided the operator in the really tricky spots. This left the clutch pedal solely for 'inching' operations, such as hitching implements.

A beefed-up version of the 4010's synchro transmission was also available for those that were sceptical of the abilities of the Powershift 'box, or purely wanted to save money. This offered eight forward and two reverse speeds.

To the left of the steering column were the hydraulic levers, providing fingertip control of load and depth control and up to three remote cylinders. The linkage had a lifting capacity of 3,790lbs – more than ample for large ploughs and cultivation equipment. A two-speed pto was fitted at the rear but, interestingly, a mid-mounted 1,000rpm pto was also present. This enabled the 4020 to operate two implements simultaneously – something we now take for granted. The pto was fully-independent, allowing the operator to change gear or stop completely without affecting the pto. This was particularly useful when baling.

In Britain the 4020 was only offered in standard configuration, but in its homeland it appeared in row-crop, row-crop tricycle and hi-crop guises too. These suited the varied crops that were grown by farmers – from maize in its delicate early stages to highly-developed sugar cane crops. The standard model was popular as it had the option of an adjustable front axle, that

The operator's clear view from the seat of the 4020. Photo: Peter D Simpson

gave widths of between 48 and 80 inches, and a bar-type rear axle that allowed the wheels to move in and out easily, whilst having the capability to accommodate either 'slim' duals or super singles.

European tractors are easily distinguished from their American cousins because of the

In the US the three-point linkage would have been fitted with a Quick Coupler, whereas in Europe it was designed to take both category I and II fittings. Photo: Peter D Simpson

mudguards. The Stateside tractors had flat-topped versions with double headlights mounted underneath, whilst the European tractors had large, curvaceous mudguards with the headlights mounted on the side panel in front of the operator's legs.

Safety frames became an option in 1966 – the Roll-Gard was available for all tractors across the range. Cabs were also available, with the 4020 receiving a self-contained unit that had heavy foam backing and wall-to-wall insulation to reduce vibration and noise ingress.

Another option introduced mid-way through production and chiefly seen in America, was front-wheel assist. This was a hydraulically-controlled system that featured compact motors inside the front hubs, giving the operator added traction at the flick of a switch. Although offering more pull than a standard two-wheel drive tractor, front-wheel assist could never match a true mechanical four-wheel drive system.

The 4020 accounted for 48 per cent of all John Deere tractor sales in North America during 1966 and was described as the jewel in the 20 Series. Deere's engineers continually strove to improve the tractor, to the extent that it became the most popular tractor of the era and one of the world's greatest classic tractors ever. ∎

The Ford 3000 was a compact machine and looked good to boot. Photo: Peter Plehov

Ford 3000 Super Dexta

Basildon, UK: 1964-1968

When Ford Tractor Operations was created in March 1961 and the Ford Tractor Division in 1962, the aim was to co-ordinate tractor engineering and manufacturing operations in England and America. The tough decision had to be made: do we go with the blue British-built tractors or the familiar grey and red tractors as built in America?

The Dagenham-built blue and grey New Performance Fordson Super Dexta and Super Major were imported into America and badged as the Ford 2000 and 5000 respectively. It was at this point that the colours for the New Performance Super tractors were decided upon. A blue tractor with grey mudguards and wheel centres would become the globally-accepted colour scheme for the new worldwide Ford range of tractors. The new range was introduced in 1964.

These two models accompanied the Ford 6000, which had been introduced in 1961, although this tractor's paint colour scheme sported grey/beige tin work and wheel centres and featured a blue chassis.

As Ford tractor production moved from Dagenham to Basildon in 1964, the new factory coincided with the launch of a new series of tractors which were introduced in America in October and shortly after to the UK market at the December Smithfield Show.

The 3000 was one of four models in Ford's new 6X range of tractors, now known as the Pre-Force range. Its stablemates, the 2000 and 4000, were three-cylinder machines and the 5000 was powered by a four-cylinder unit – and all featured a bold new blue and white livery. So as not to alienate farmers completely, Ford opted to retain its previous naming policy at home and overseas, with tractors having both a name and a number – in this case, the Ford 3000 Super Dexta.

Technical specification

Produced:	1964-1968
Engine:	Ford 175 CID
Cylinders:	3
Bore x stroke:	4.2in x 4.2in
Displacement:	175cu in
Torque:	115.8lb ft @1,400rpm
Horsepower:	46hp
Transmission:	8 forward, 2 reverse
Speed range:	1.37mph – 17.4mph
Linkage:	Category I & II
Lift capacity:	2,800lbs
Weight:	3,505bs
Tyre sizes:	Front: 5.50x16
	Rear: 11x28

Along with many other tractors of the period, the 3000 had a dual-range gearbox of the constant mesh type with four forward and one reverse speed in each of the high and low ranges, but could be purchased with the optional Select-O-Speed. This was a clutch-less, 10-forward, 2-reverse-speed transmission that offered an independent 540rpm pto or, in the case of the deluxe version, a tri-speed pto (ground/540/1,000rpm). Motion was controlled via a hand selector beneath the steering wheel, but a pedal was provided for inching operations, such as hitching to implements.

The advantage Select-O-Speed tractors had over their Multi-Power-equipped MF counterparts was engine braking in every gear and a useful 'park' feature that locked the rear wheels as a safety measure. Irrespective of the transmission specified, the 3000 came equipped with a differential lock as standard.

The standard Ford 3000 was offered to the farmer at a little under £900 whereas the option of having the Select-O-Speed transmission fitted added a further £180. Due to the high reputation of the Fordson range of tractors, once word leaked out about the new Basildon range of tractors, order books quickly filled – even though no-one knew quite what the new range of tractors was going to look like or even the final specifications.

Ford was rightly proud of its 'square'-design engine and there's no doubt that it had a lively character – although it could never really match the low down lugging ability of tractors equipped with long-stroke engines. With 46hp available to the operator from a 175cu in engine, the little 3000 Super Dexta had plenty to offer and was usually seen paired with a two or three-furrow conventional plough, but was known to be used with a five-furrow Ransomes TS 78 plough by some farmers. The tractor, naturally, benefited from additional front-end ballast when lifting such a heavy implement – but the added weight on the rear axle significantly ➡

This nicely-restored 3000 has the optional Select-O-Speed transmission – note the lever below the steering wheel. Photo: Peter Plehov

So as not to alienate farmers completely, Ford opted to retain its previous naming policy at home and overseas, with tractors having both a name and a number – in this case, the Ford 3000 Super Dexta

The unusual silencer was a feature of the smaller Ford Pre-Force models. Photo: Peter Plehov

improved traction and the 3000 just dug in and got on with the job in hand.

The 3000 was equipped with fully-independent hydraulics and a dual-category linkage that permitted the use of larger implements, while having an automatic pick-up hitch and power-assisted steering among the list of popular options. Interestingly, unlike other tractors of the period, a swinging drawbar and clevis were not standard equipment and had to be specified from the options list, either as a separate system, or in conjunction with the automatic pick-up hitch.

Mid-way through production, Roadless Traction decided that it would capitalise

on the success of the 3000 by offering a four-wheel drive version of the tractor – the Ploughmaster 46 introduced in 1966. It utilised the same Selene system as used on the Roadless Dexta, albeit with different ratios, and cost just over £1,500. For those that already owned a Ford 3000, a conversion kit could be bought for less than £600.

With the introduction of the 6X Series Ford saw worldwide sales soar year on year. Within a couple of years the Ford Tractor Division had its best ever tractor sales. With new markets opening up worldwide, many machines were adapted for specialist uses such as narrow models

for vineyards and orchards, while other conversions suited the crops grown with row-crop and hi-clearance options. Many other interesting conversions were undertaken by independent manufacturers.

The year 1968 did not spell the end for the inimitable 3000. In fact, the 6Y – or Force range of tractors as they are known – was produced until 1975, of which the 3000 was part. The new tractor featured various refinements and options and, some would say, improved styling. The Super Dexta name would be dropped from the side of the bonnet and the range would also be joined by a bigger brother, the turbocharged 7000, several years later, in 1971. ■

The stunning grounds of Castle Archdale make the perfect backdrop for Adrian Abraham's MF 135. Photo: Gary Connolly

Massey Ferguson 135

Coventry, UK: 1964-1978

The best-selling Massey Ferguson tractor of all time – what better way to introduce one of the most iconic machines in agricultural history? The 135 is a true legend, a symbol of farming in Sixties and Seventies Britain. The tractor had a fine heritage and epitomised all that was good about small tractors, managing to encompass all of Harry Ferguson's initial ideas, whilst incorporating new features and improvements wherever possible.

Although the company's previous models had sold well, MF was keen to rationalise its range of tractors and so set its engineers to work on a new line-up. The 100 Series, or Red Giants as they were known, were launched to the Press at the 1964 Smithfield

Show, but went on sale in 1965 to high acclaim. The 135 was the smallest British-built tractor in the range, with the little, French-built 130 as the only smaller machine.

In mechanical terms it closely resembled its predecessor, the 35X, but radical new styling brought it into line with current trends. The Perkins A3.152-powered 35s were noted for their excellent starting characteristics and good lugging power, but the 135 took this a step further with the introduction of the AD3.152 engine. This was a direct-injection unit that produced 45.5hp and a memorable noise to go along with it! Further refinements would see the engine pushing out 47hp at 2,250rpm and 131lb/ft of torque at 1,300rpm. It should be said that the 135 was available in petrol form, but relatively few were sold.

At a time when more and more manufacturers were either testing or

actually offering synchromesh transmissions, MF opted to retain the bulletproof six-by-two system used in the 35. It was a practical gearbox that offered a good range of speeds for both field and road work, but was further enhanced by the addition of Multi-Power. This doubled the number of speeds and gave a useful 21.7mph on 11x28 rear tyres but, as some farmers found to their cost, there was no engine braking in low range. A dual clutch was standard – which was particularly useful when the operator needed to stop the tractor, but not the pto-powered implement. Letting a large swath pass through the baler is the obvious scenario, but the dual clutch was a godsend when using many other pieces of machinery. A single clutch was an option, reducing the overall cost of the tractor.

The engine was, of course, excellent but a good tractor of the day was nothing without its three-point linkage. The diminutive 135's hitch was built around the Ferguson System – offering draft and position control with a 2,850lbs lift capacity. Pressure control was also offered enabling the tractor, with the aid of a coupler (provided at no extra cost) consisting of a three-point mounted frame and chain that was slung under the implement's drawbar, to operate trailed equipment and keep going through ➥

When it was launched, the 135 featured the same swept-back axle as the 35 – giving a turning circle of 19 feet 3 inches, but this was later replaced by a straight version that increased the turning circle by 6 inches

These MF 135s look similar but are actually quite different. The front tractor dates from 1973, but was refurbished by Massey Ferguson in 1994, using parts initially destined for a 240 model. It was sold at auction when the Banner Lane factory closed in 2006. Photo: Jonathan Whitlam

even the toughest conditions. This worked via a constant lift being exerted on the lower links – ranging from 150psi to 2,300psi – which meant that when operating at maximum, the weight on the rear wheels could be almost doubled, thus increasing traction. The other advantage the 135 had over its predecessor in this

department was the addition of response control – housed in a small quadrant to the inside of the driver's right shin.

When it was launched, the 135 featured the same swept-back axle as the 35 – giving a turning circle of 19 feet 3 inches, but this was later replaced by a straight version that increased the turning circle by 6 inches.

Just two-and-a-half turns were needed to get the steering wheel from lock to lock.

The new styling of the 100 Series tractors saw a square-cut bonnet across the range and flat-topped mudguards on the bigger tractors, but the 135 and the smaller 130 had shell-type mudguards like the 35. Some thought it odd that a straight bonnet should

be used alongside curved mudguards, but this feature was complemented nicely by silver-rimmed wheels featuring red centres.

The styling was changed on later tractors and the flat-topped mudguards of the larger tractors now appeared on the 135. At first, these featured beautiful, bolt-on, aluminium grab handles to the front – now highly-prized by enthusiasts – but these were later replaced by integrated pressed steel versions. After the change from shell-type to flat-topped mudguards tractors were, on the whole, fitted with all-silver wheels, but some still featured the red and silver versions. The optional Power Adjusted Variable Track (PAVT) wheels were always produced with silver rims and red centres.

With the increasing popularity of after-market, 'will fit' cabs from manufacturers such as Lambourn, Massey Ferguson was quick to realise the potential of offering its own version and with the arrival of the flat-topped mudguards was able to do just that. The steel-framed, fibreglass cab was ➡

A combination such as this would have been commonplace on farms all over Britain. Photo: Gary Connolly

roomy, practical and an attractive alternative and, as it was designed in-house, enabled full access to the battery and fuel tank.

About a decade later, the Flexi-cab was launched. It too was steel-framed, but had a canvas/tarpaulin outer skin. It looked as good, if not better, than its rigid predecessor and was somewhat quieter that the now-famous 'bubble'.

On later tractors a QD, or Quick-Detach, cab was offered that had specially-designed mudguards that facilitated removal of the top portion in under ten minutes. It was designed to comply with the 90dB noise level legislation and featured sound-proofing, windows which could be opened and lifting eyes. The design meant that to take away the upper segment, only eight bolts and one electrical connection had to be removed.

The 135 was, and still is, mostly found in standard form – but its versatility and good features meant that it was the perfect base for many other applications. A vineyard version was offered by MF, that had the capability of operating between 30in and 60in track widths – with many fruit growers in Britain finding it to be the perfect tractor for working among apple trees.

Its compact size and capable engine made the 135 the ideal skid-unit for many other applications – and not just MF-derived products. Standen used 35s on its early self-propelled sugar beet harvesters and after the launch of the 135, the new tractor seemed to be the obvious choice for a replacement. The little MF was also used as a base for reverse-drive forklifts and backhoe loaders by some companies, but found uses in many other applications – both agricultural and industrial.

Numerous options were available for the 135, from larger wheels and tyres to a cigarette lighter, or suspension seat to horizontal exhaust – what the farmer wanted, he could generally have! A pick-up hitch and Multi-Power were perhaps the most common choices from the options list, but expect to find many tractors fitted with as many 'bells and whistles' as are conceivable. With the recent trend in concours restorations and in the hope that their tractor will stand out from the crowd, many enthusiasts have made it their aim to equip their 135 with as many optional extras as they can find!

The MF 135 has always been popular and current trends suggest that interest won't wane. Many farmers still use them for light jobs around the farm and enthusiasts love them as they are perfect for ploughing matches and road runs, whilst being easy to work on and light enough to transport to shows easily. Wherever your allegiances lie, you'll find it difficult to deny that the Massey Ferguson 135 is a very good tractor – with well over 350,000 units sold its popularity speaks for itself! ∎

Technical specification

Produced:	1964-1978
Engine:	Perkins AD3.152
Cylinders:	3
Bore x stroke:	3.6in x 5in
Displacement:	152.6cu in
Torque:	119lb ft @1,300rpm
Horsepower:	45.5hp
Transmission:	6 forward, 2 reverse
	12 forward, 4 reverse (Multi-Power)
Speed range:	0.3mph – 16.8mph
	0.4mph – 21.7mph (Multi-Power)
Linkage:	Category I
Lift capacity:	2,850lbs (later 3,150lbs)
Weight:	3,200lbs
Tyre sizes:	Front: 6.00x16
	Rear: 11x28

MASSEY FERGUSON

The Genuine Choice

AGCO PARTS

THINK RED
THINK SUPPORT

VISION INNOVATION **SUPPORT** LEADERSHIP QUALITY RELIABILITY PRIDE COMMITMENT

A cost effective investment

If you own a Ferguson or Massey Ferguson tractor then you won't need reminding about the great asset you have on your hands. With due care and attention older tractors will give you many more years of faithful service.

Everything from simple preventative maintenance through to complete restoration is a worthy investment. With Genuine Massey Ferguson **10+** Parts, backed up by the expertise of your MF dealer, it's now very affordable.

10+ Parts from Massey Ferguson

- Specifically designed for tractors and combines over 10 years old
- Complete machine range MF 35 to MF 8100 series tractors and MF 24 to MF 800 series combines
- Massey Ferguson engineering approved
- Value for money, economical repair
- Permanently low prices!

10+

Supporting your Massey Ferguson machine whatever its age!

Contact your Massey Ferguson dealer today for details of some great **10+** deals or click on www.masseyferguson.com to find your nearest MF dealer.

It was a chunky, square-cut machine with a high driving position offering good all-round visibility

Oliver 1750

Charles City, Iowa, USA: 1966-1969

owadays we think of six-cylinder tractors as the mainstay of most farming operations – but in the 1960s they were still considered to be big machines. Machines of 120hp are now largely standard, but back then 80hp was considered to be more than enough for even the largest farms. A modern tractor of 80hp would usually be seen with a three or four-furrow plough, depending on soil conditions, whereas an 80hp tractor in the 1960s would be seen with a five or six-furrow plough.

One such tractor is the Oliver 1750 – a well-liked machine in America and one that is becoming popular in Britain with the ever-increasing trend of importing. The 1750 was, and in some cases still is, considered to be a good all-rounder – a jack-of-all-trades. With almost 70hp at the pto it was ideal for swathing cereal crops and maize cutting, while the addition of four-wheel drive made it the ideal tractor for pulling a semi-mounted plough.

At the 1750's launch in 1966, two years after the first tractors in the 50 Series, a choice of engines was available – a 283cu in petrol or a 310cu in diesel.

These were Waukesha-Oliver units, that had been used in the outgoing 1800 model, rated at 2,400rpm.

The vast majority of farmers chose to equip their 1750 with the optional Hydra-Power Drive that offered 12 forward and two reverse speeds. It was a hydraulically-actuated transmission that allowed forward speed to be reduced and torque increased at the touch of a lever. Shifting was hydraulic, which permitted 'feathering' – enabling easy starting under load – and easy down-shifting when the operator encountered a tough patch.

The 1750 had a choice of three pto options – a 540rpm unit, 1,000rpm unit or a dual-speed system that was easily switched between the two speeds by removing a circlip and changing the shaft.

Oliver's real coup was the choice of clearance options. Standard two-wheel drive and mechanical front-wheel drive

wheel drive counterpart, added stability on hills, an in-built braking system on steep slopes and extra weight – helping the tractor to accommodate larger implements.

The styling of the 1750 was, some say, an acquired taste – but was largely accepted by the farming fraternity. It was a chunky, square-cut machine with a high driving position offering good all-round visibility. The flat-topped mudguards housed the headlights, leaving the cast-iron grille to aid cooling and provide inherent ballast.

Oliver was purchased by the White Motor Corporation (WMC), to be joined in 1962 by the Cockshutt Farm Equipment Company and Minneapolis-Moline a year later. With the formation of the White Farm Equipment Company in 1969, production would became standardised across the brands and badge-engineering became the norm. This meant that parts were readily available from many dealers, not just Oliver agents, increasing the popularity of tractors such as the six-cylinder 1750.

Farmers loved the tractor's rugged construction and reliability, with many choosing to keep their 1960s Oliver 1750 rather than trade it in for a modern machine. Many continue to provide excellent service across the United States of America and those that do become available are quickly snapped up by enthusiasts and farmers looking to add to their fleet of green and white tractors. ■

Technical specification

Produced:	1966-1969
Engine:	Waukesha-Oliver
Cylinders:	6
Bore x stroke:	Petrol: 3.875in x 4in
	Diesel: 3.875in x 4.375in
Displacement:	Petrol: 283cu in
	Diesel: 310cu in
Torque:	Unknown
	Unknown
Horsepower:	80hp
Transmission:	12 forward, 2 reverse
Speed range:	1.2mph – 14.5mph
Linkage:	Category II
Lift capacity:	4,000lbs
Weight:	2WD: 9,760lbs
	4WD: Unknown
Tyre sizes:	2WD: Front: 7.50x15
	Rear: 18.4x38
	4WD: Front: 16.9x28
	Rear: 18.4x38

A two-wheel drive Oliver 1750 with a Rock-O-Matic on stone picking duties in New York State. Photo: Peter D Simpson

A mechanical front-wheel drive Oliver 1750 with four-furrow semi-mounted plough in New York State. Photo: Peter D Simpson

were commonplace, but a whole host of other variants was available. A Wheatland model was the popular choice for prairie operations, while the Ricefield option offered increased clearance in standing crops and the Row-crop model came with a choice of four front ends. There was a standard adjustable axle, a narrow adjustable derivative, a tricycle-type arrangement and dual front wheels.

Not satisfied with one four-wheel drive option, Oliver opted to give farmers a choice of mechanical or hydraulic front-wheel drive. Mechanical front-wheel drive naturally offered the strongest assistance, while the hydraulic system was more of an aid than a true pulling axle. Hydraulic assistance was obviously a cheaper option than mechanical front-wheel, but could never offer the benefits of the more expensive system. These were four-fold: a 25 per cent increase in pull over its two-

A pristine Roadless 4WD tractor owned by Gerry Gallagher of Drumquin. Photo: Gary Connolly

the lower links were connected, and then be reflected via a series of linkages to the hydraulic system – raising the implement slightly to overcome the obstacle and therefore keeping the draft load constant. This process happened very fast, but was smooth in its operation, only being noticeable to the operator through a gentle 'twitching' felt through the seat. This, along with the tractor's 6,546lb bulk, gave the operator the ability to achieve a level field even in the most demanding soil conditions.

The rest of the tractor was standard fair, if not over-engineered, with the mindset

McCormick IH 634

Doncaster, UK: 1968-1972

In the years prior to the launch of the 634, International Harvester had enjoyed success with both of its previous 'big-hitters' – the B-450 and the B-614 – and the new model was supposed to build on this success, which in many ways it did. The fundamental problem was that compared to rival manufacturers' models, the 634 was rather archaic and some farmers couldn't see past the fact that the tractor's roots lay in a different era of farming.

Those who could see the benefits of proven, if not somewhat basic, technology were rewarded with a tractor that had the ability to operate large soil-engaging implements in heavy conditions – largely thanks to the combination of the indirect injection BD-281 engine and the torsion bar draft control system.

The tractor shared its 66hp engine with the BTD-8 crawler, among others, and despite its relatively modest power, had the ability to produce phenomenal torque at

only 1,200rpm. Besides this, a large bore and long stroke gave the 634 a unique sound – almost a bellow – which is something to savour when the tractor is pulling hard.

The tractor had few vices, but ask anyone to name a negative point about the 634 and virtually everyone will mention its inability to start satisfactorily. International Harvester claimed, "All-weather electric starting via glow-plugs ensures reliable instant power, even in cold weather". How the company was allowed to claim this is almost beyond belief, as the 634 became renowned for needing an excellent battery, or two, to get enough heat into the glow-plugs and turn the engine quickly enough to get it up and running. Even when new, the BD-281 would initially run on three cylinders before picking up sufficiently enough for the fourth to kick-in!

One of the tractor's saving graces was its hydraulic system and it is claimed that the 634 was the first British tractor with exclusive torsion bar draft control. Under load, when ploughing for instance, the change in draft would gently twist a splined shaft, to which

Howard Sherren's 1971 IH 634 has recently undergone an extensive restoration. Photo: Howard Sherren

seemingly being that the 634 should be robust and capable of withstanding whatever the most demanding operators could throw at it. The output from the engine was channelled through a 13in Borg and Beck Dyna-life clutch with IH opting to put power to the wheels through a simple two-range, four-speed gearbox and bull gear arrangement.

The standard, two-wheel drive, 634 was more than capable of handling a five-furrow semi-mounted plough, but for those who demanded more performance, two options were available. The first was the four-wheel drive model, built with Roadless components and the second was the all-wheel drive, equal-sized wheel model built with components supplied by County Commercial Cars. Many of these tractors saw use in forestry applications where its pulling power could be optimised without the measly steering lock compromising its abilities.

Less than 4,000 634s were built, in all guises, making the tractor a comparative rarity to other IH models and as a result it has become something of a cult classic and highly desirable to collectors. ◼

> ... and despite its relatively modest power, had the ability to produce phenomenal torque at only 1,200rpm

Technical specification

Produced:	1968-1972
Engine:	IH BD-281
Cylinders:	4
Bore x stroke:	4.125in x 5.25in
Displacement:	281cu in
Torque:	225lb ft @1,200rpm
Horsepower:	66hp
Transmission:	8 forward, 2 reverse
Speed range:	0.6mph – 15.7mph
Linkage:	Category II
Lift capacity:	5,000lbs
Weight:	2WD: 6,546lbs
	4WD: 7,964lbs
	AWD: 9,572lbs
Tyre sizes:	2WD: Front: 7.50x16
	Rear: 12x38 or 13.6x38
	4WD: Front: 10x24
	Rear: 12x38 or 14x34
	AWD: Front: 12x38
	Rear: 12x38

Phillip Swales' Track-Marshall 75 is used every year with a Dowdeswell DP1 four-furrow plough. Photo: Scott Lambert

Track-Marshall 75

Gainsborough, UK: 1968-1975

rack-Marshall's machines were always popular and the 75 was no exception – particularly as it was a middle-of-the-range model. The company's crawlers had gained an excellent reputation and for those looking for a replacement for their 70 model or International Harvester BTD-8, the T-M 75 was the obvious choice.

The smallest in the Track-Marshall range, the 56, was powered by a Perkins four-cylinder unit, while the 75 and its bigger brother, the 90, were powered by the well-liked Perkins 6.354 engine. The Peterborough-built straight-six had been used in other agricultural applications and as it developed 75hp at 1,700rpm, it was the obvious choice to power the new crawler. Incidentally, the engine developed 90hp at 2,250rpm in the T-M 90.

It is worth mentioning that there were two variants of the 75 model – the C and the H. Both machines were identical in appearance, but differed in the way that they were steered, with the C utilising the finger-light balanced power steering system and the H using hydraulic clutches.

Farmers bought crawlers for improved traction in heavy conditions and to minimise ground compaction – and despite weighing well over six-and-a-half tons, the 75 only exerted 6.24lb/sq in of ground pressure. This was less than the 56 model and gave the crawler an excellent selling point, particularly when salesmen were trying to sell to farmers who were looking for a machine to prepare seedbeds.

Having said this the T-M 75 was the ideal machine for primary cultivations, too, as a three-point linkage could be specified. Marshall-Fowler claimed that the 75's predecessor, the 70, was "the first farming

wanting to keep their ear drums and sanity intact would have needed ear defenders – but this was typical for cabs around at the time. Many commented that the cab detracted from the good looks of the 75, but given a choice of aesthetics over being warm and dry, most chose the latter!

Other useful options were available to those wanting to spec-up their 75, including a pto, winch, street plates and a range of hydraulically-operated front and rear-mounted equipment – such as dozer blades and excavators. Most 75s were bought with a three-point linkage and cab, but it was not uncommon for farmers to buy a crawler solely with a drawbar. Many had previously invested in tool carriers for their old crawlers and so felt they could not justify the extra expense of specifying a three-point linkage. In 1975 a Track-Marshall 75 cost £9,174, with a three-point linkage and front weights adding an extra £1,429 to the price. A cab with four worklights and sound insulation set the farmer back a further £453.

Due to this high price tag most farmers kept their 75s for many years, with some continuing to own them even now – using them for winter ploughing or extracting tractors from the mire. They were well-liked because of their rugged construction and reliable engine, with many clocking in excess of 5,000 hours. Their popularity makes it difficult to find one in preservation, as they are still considered a useful workhorse around the farm, and their huge weight makes transportation somewhat complicated. If you are lucky enough to see a Track-Marshall 75 at work, take the time to watch and listen to it – as it's not something you'll see every day. ■

Technical specification

Produced:	1968-1975
Engine:	Perkins 6.354
Cylinders:	6
Bore x stroke:	3.875in x 5in
Displacement:	354cu in
Torque:	Unknown
Horsepower:	75hp
Transmission:	5 forward, 3 reverse
Speed range:	1.9mph – 5.9mph
Linkage:	Category II/III
Lift capacity:	Unknown
Weight:	14,886lbs
Track size:	16in

In 1975, a three-point linkage would have added an extra £1,429 to the price of a T-M 75. Photo: Scott Lambert

crawler to successfully operate a fully-versatile hydraulic three-point linkage" and that the new crawler took this technology a step further with improved hydraulics and either category II or III attachment capability. This meant that farmers could operate mounted or semi-mounted ploughs that were usually only deemed suitable for wheeled tractors in excess of 100hp.

In terms of styling the 75 was a striking machine with a 'bullet hole' grille, reminiscent of early David Brown tractors, and angular tin work that brought the styling in-line with current trends. It has to be said that the optional cab, like so many others of the period, left much to be desired – both in looks and comfort. It was essentially a sheet metal structure that had roof-mounted work lights and hinged doors. It was a hot and noisy addition to the 75 that was only really good for keeping the rain off and the wind out. Those

Tony Nyquist aboard his newly-restored Leyland 154 in Australia. Photo: Courtesy of Tony Nyquist

Leyland 154

Bathgate, UK: 1969-1979

lthough the diminutive Leyland 154 was launched in 1969, its origins can be traced back to the BMC Mini of 1965. This compact, 15hp machine was a product of the Harry Ferguson Research company – and featured a 1.49 litre BMC A Series diesel engine, but was also available in 20hp petrol form.

The Mini was sold alongside the popular Nuffield range of the time, but appealed to local authorities more than farmers, due to its limited capacity. It was the perfect tractor for cutting grass in parks and gardens, whilst finding favour with market gardeners who needed a small tractor to operate in and around greenhouses.

In 1968 a BMC B Series engine of 25hp was fitted under the Mini's bonnet, with the tractor being re-badged as the Nuffield 4/25. The model remained popular but production was short-lived, as the striking orange livery of the Nuffield range was replaced by Leyland blue – the Nuffield 4/25 was now the Leyland 154.

When it was launched in 1969 the 154 only cost £640, whilst its stablemates – the 344 and 384 – cost £1,080 and £1,186 respectively. As was the case when the 154 was orange, it was never intended to be popular with large-acreage farmers – and was aimed squarely at the municipal and horticultural sectors, with a choice of 25hp diesel or 28hp petrol powerplants. A narrow version was introduced in 1971 that appealed to vineyard and

orchard owners, but few were sold in comparison to the standard tractor.

The starting problems that would beset many tractors of the era were shared by the BMC diesel engine, in that turning the key and driving off was never going to be possible. The operator's manual recommended heating the glow-plugs for 30 seconds before engaging the starter, but in reality this often had to be doubled to ensure that enough heat got into the plugs.

Once up and running, the engine more than redeemed itself. It was powerful, but frugal and managed to produce maximum torque at a reasonably modest 1,750rpm. It won many hearts with its gutsy attitude which when coupled to the brilliant transmission, made operating the tractor easy and stress-free. The nine-by-three 'box was of the constant mesh, sliding collar type and provided a well-spaced range of speeds from delicate greenhouse operations to sprints between city centre parks. Unlike some of its competitors, the little Leyland also had the ability to stop swiftly! The double disc brake system

Technical specification

Produced:	1969-1979
Engine:	BMC 15T diesel
Cylinders:	4
Bore x stroke:	2.875in x 3.5in
Displacement:	90.8cu in
Torque:	61lb ft @1,750rpm
Horsepower:	25hp
Transmission:	9 forward, 3 reverse
Speed range:	0.9mph – 14.1mph
Linkage:	Category I
Lift capacity:	1,000lbs
Weight:	2,325lbs
Tyre sizes:	Front: 5.00x15
	Rear: 11.2x24

With a modest lift capacity, the 154 was the ideal tractor for a two-furrow plough or mower. Photo: Courtesy of Tony Nyquist

was far superior to the drums used on the MF 135 for example and meant that the 154 could come to a stop with only light pressure exerted on the brake pedal.

The Leyland had another ace up its sleeve in that it offered a two-speed pto, a feature usually only seen on bigger tractors. This coupled with an ample lift capacity, live drive and good draft control made the 154 a capable little machine. It was overlooked by many who dismissed its capabilities due to its size – but those who did buy the tractor found it to be more than adequate for undertaking light tasks.

The 154 has since won a new army of fans that see it is a viable second-hand alternative to the barrage of Japanese compact machines that have become the vogue in recent years. Its light weight makes it perfect for mowing without scuffing the grass too much, whilst being reliable, simple to maintain and not too thirsty. The Leyland 154 was a trendsetter – the low-horsepower compact tractor of its day. ■

It was powerful, but frugal and managed to produce maximum torque at a reasonably modest 1,750rpm

The Leyland 154 was perfect for undertaking small jobs around the farm. Photo: Courtesy of Jonathan Whitlam and Stephen Richmond

The existing 5000-spec linkage was given an assistor ram to enable it to cope with heavy implements.
Photo: Peter D Simpson

Ford 7000

Basildon, UK: 1971-1975

aunched at the 1971 Smithfield Show, the Ford 7000 caused a stir and was an instant triumph as it was a high-horsepower machine in a relatively compact form. It was also the first British mass-produced tractor to feature a turbocharger, although some specialist conversion companies used a turbocharged version of the Ford 5000 skid-unit in their machines. Prior to its launch, farmers of the blue persuasion either had to make do with the 75hp 5000 or stump up the cash for the six-cylinder 8000 – rated at 115hp.

The success of the 7000 was largely attributed to the fact that it was essentially an uprated 5000 – a tractor that had already established itself in the market and was popular with Britain's farming community. The 5000 was a compact machine and by shoehorning a turbocharger under the bonnet, Ford was able to add an extra dimension to what was already a highly-accomplished tractor.

Of course, the 19hp increase over its smaller sibling was a great addition, but the 7000 also had another ace up its sleeve. Its new Load Monitor hydraulic system was something of a revelation in that it enabled the operator to have fully-regulated draft control over both mounted and semi-mounted implements. The engine's power meant that the tractor had the guts to pull larger implements, but the existing 5000-spec linkage was uprated with an assistor

farmsteads and with contractors – who had been crying out for a compact powerhouse for some time. Paired with a three or four-furrow reversible plough, or anything up to a six-furrow semi-mounted plough, the 7000 was the perfect tool for cultivating large areas in double-quick time.

As it was based on the 5000, the tractor was also popular with dealers – as it enabled them to market a bigger machine whilst having the opportunity to utilise the back-up parts which were already on their shelves for the rest of the range. It would also prove a hit with the likes of specialist firms, such as County and Roadless, who saw it as the ideal skid-unit to create a four-wheel drive, high-horsepower tractor that would appeal to forestry contractors and owners of farms with heavy soil conditions. Roadless, naturally, opted for the unequal-size-wheel option in the form of the Duncan-cabbed 94T, whilst the County 944 had equal-sized wheels and a Hara safety cab.

Externally the 7000 looked remarkably like the 5000, but with one or two exceptions. The most obvious differences were the bonnet decals and the addition of a tall, air pre-cleaner pipe with dust bowl mounted on top. Many 7000s were also adorned with wheel weights, front and rear, and either the slab-style weights that appeared on the New Performance Super Major and the like, or the suitcase-style weights that are now commonplace.

Later tractors had the option of a two-speed pto and Dual Power transmission – a gearbox that gained popularity in future years. The pto options, coupled with the power on-hand from the turbocharged

Technical specification	
Produced:	1971-1975
Engine:	Ford 256 CID
Cylinders:	4 (turbocharged)
Bore x stroke:	4.4in x 4.2in
Displacement:	256cu in
Torque:	240lb ft @1,600rpm
Horsepower:	94hp
Transmission:	8 forward, 2 reverse
Speed range:	0.8mph – 16.8mph
Linkage:	Category II
Lift capacity:	5,291lbs
Weight:	6,300lbs
Tyre sizes:	Front: 7.50x18
	Rear: 14x34

engine, meant that the 7000 was the boss of whatever it was coupled to – be it mower, baler, rotovator or power-sapping forage harvester. The big advantage the Dual Power system had over Massey Ferguson's Multi-Power unit was engine braking in both ranges – sixteen forward and four reverse gears were on-hand to provide a multitude of speeds for an infinite number of jobs.

Despite its popularity, the 7000 was never going to be Ford's best seller, as it was just too big for the majority of farmers. The three-cylinder 4000 was still the ➡

ram to enable it to cope with the heavy reversible ploughs that were now in vogue.

It wasn't all plain sailing though as the excellent hydraulic system was, in some cases, the 7000's downfall. With salesmen over-promoting the machine's back-end capabilities, some farmers saw this as an invitation to hitch-up the largest implement they could lay their hands on. This, inevitably, had dire consequences for the tractor – but was the only blemish on the otherwise excellent reputation enjoyed by the 7000.

At just over £2,700, the 7000 was out of reach of many smallholders and low-acreage farmers, but it proved to be a popular tool with owners of significant

Additional ballast and the tall air pre-cleaner gave the 7000 a purposeful look. Photo: Peter D Simpson

... the 7000 was the perfect tool for cultivating large areas in double-quick time

The Ford 7000 is as popular now as it ever was. Photo: Peter D Simpson

ideal tractor for the masses, but with farmers increasing their acreages and contractors looking to gain a foothold on large estates, the 7000 would always have a place on the large farm. The tractor was only produced for four years before it was

superseded by the 7600 – essentially the same tractor underneath a different skin, but with a 3hp increase in engine power.

Although the same size as a 5000, the larger standard tyres, added ballast and prominent air pre-cleaner gave the 7000

a purposeful look and an impression of greater size than was actually the case. It captured the hearts of many and now commands a premium amongst collectors and restorers who want something special for rallies and working days. ■

This impressive 1977 Roadless 120 is used by David Leech to plough many acres each year. Photo: Peter D Simpson

Roadless 120

Hounslow, UK: 1971-1983

The first thing that you noticed about the Roadless 120 was its wheels. Unlike many of its stablemates, it featured equal-sized wheels and looked more like a County tractor than a Roadless. It did, however, like the vast majority of the Hounslow-built models, feature many Ford components – including an excellent engine from Ford's industrial division.

It was the engine that actually spawned the 120, as the fitting of the new 2715E motor to the 115 model allowed Roadless to offer a 'new' tractor. The 120hp, six-cylinder lump was introduced by Ford in the early months of 1971, giving Roadless the time to adopt the engine, fit it to their tractor and thoroughly test it before the 120's launch at the Smithfield Show at the end of the year.

This excellent engine was coupled to the transmission from a Ford 7600 tractor – a gearbox capable of withstanding the

stresses generated by the big engine. This unit had its origins in the Ford 5000 and went on to be used in the turbocharged 7000 model and was so good that Ford decided to add the popular Dual Power function, a 'splitter' that increased the number of gears to 16 forward and 4 reverse.

The 120 did, of course, have the upper hand over its unequal-size-wheeled siblings when it came to traction. True four-wheel drive meant that it was always going to perform better than a 94T for example, but manoeuvrability would be its downfall. Much like the Dutra D4K-B, the 120's engine was mounted well forward – placing added ballast over the driven axle. In effect, approximately 60 per cent of the tractor's weight was at the front, but this was balanced to near-perfect

Technical specification

Produced:	1971-1983
Engine:	Ford 2715E
	Ford 2725
Cylinders:	6
Bore x stroke:	Ford 2715E: 4.22in x 4.52in
	Ford 2725: 4.22in x 4.52in
Displacement:	Ford 2715E: 380cu in
	Ford 2725: 380cu in
Torque:	Ford 2715E: 280lb ft @1,600rpm
	Ford 2725: Unknown
Horsepower:	Ford 2715E: 120hp
	Ford 2725: 130hp
Transmission:	16 forward, 4 reverse
Speed range:	1.4mph – 19.8mph
Linkage:	Category II
Lift capacity:	9,392lbs
Weight:	10,730lbs
Tyre sizes:	Front: 12x38 or 14x34
	Rear: 12x38 or 14x34

weight distribution with the addition of a large plough or rigid-tine cultivator.

The early 120 models, along with many other Roadless tractors, were fitted with Duncan cabs to coincide with the newly-imposed safety regulations – but as time went on Roadless decided that the Aberdeen-built unit was somewhat primitive and searched for a new cab supplier that could fulfil its needs. The lucky company was Lambourn Engineering, based in Newbury, which won the contract to supply cabs that would be fitted to the vast majority of Roadless models over the coming years. From 1977 Roadless made the Lambourn LFQ unit a standard fitment across the entire range and, either by luck or judgement, this coincided with the celebrations that marked the Queen's Silver Jubilee – leading the new tractors to be dubbed the J Series. As is usually the case, refinements were made that included the addition of gas struts to the doors and hinged side windows, rather than the sliding type previously fitted. In the latter half of 1978, tractors featuring

this new cab were designated the K Series.

Some of the last 120s built were fitted with the 130hp Ford 2725 engine and the arrival of Ford's 10 Series meant that the freshly-styled tractors would require a new designation. Designated the S Series, these tractors retained the white bonnet and blue cab of their predecessors, but had the curved tin work and new grille of Ford's latest models. Of the last three tractors to leave the factory, two were 120 S Series models – one, the last tractor ever to be sold by Roadless, went to British Telecom and the other, sold by the company's liquidators, went to an arable farmer.

The 120 was by no means cheap – with a J series model costing just over £16,000. This type of expenditure could be justified by large-acreage farmers and contractors who knew that the tractor would eventually pay for itself. Nowadays, it is not uncommon for Roadless tractors to sell for £10,000 or more, depending on condition – but with less than 60 examples of the 120 built, prices for these can be very high indeed. ■

> … it featured equal-sized wheels and looked more like a County tractor than a Roadless

When coupled to this Ransomes Överum five-furrow reversible plough, David Leech says that the Roadless 120 is perfectly balanced. Photo: Peter D Simpson

This 1974 John Deere 3130 is owned by Phillip Swales of Cambridgeshire. Photo: Scott Lambert

John Deere 3130

Mannheim, Germany: 1972-1979

The first incarnation of the 3130 was arguably the more attractive of the two to roll out of the Mannheim factory. The 'horseshoe' bonnet of the New Generation model was the same as that used on the 20 Series tractors that preceded it and was well-liked by most operators. It bore more than a passing resemblance to the 3120, but substituted the 303D engine for the 6329D – which developed a further 8hp at 1,000rpm less.

It's not often that a tractor is praised for its looks as much as its competence in the field, but the New Generation 3130 was a stunning machine – everything about it oozed sophistication. A simple livery enhanced the clean and flowing lines, with beautifully-crafted mesh side-grilles aiding ventilation to the six-cylinder engine. Even the exhaust system was a work of art – with the manifold more akin to a sculpture and an oval-shaped, matt-black silencer crowning the bonnet. Unfortunately, many tractors were fitted with cabs made by Alexander Duncan which spoiled the lines of the tractor somewhat.

Looks obviously don't signify a great tractor, but with the excellent twelve-by-six transmission and plenty of power on tap, the 3130 was always destined to be well-liked by farmers because of its silky-smooth engine and impressive lift capabilities. It was common for the 3130 to be paired with a four-furrow conventional plough but, where conditions allowed, a five-furrow semi-mounted plough was often used.

The biggest change to the 3130 came in 1975 when the tractor was completely restyled to match those built at Deere's Waterloo facility in Iowa. All European-built tractors lost the 'horseshoe' bonnet and gained integral headlights and an altogether more contemporary look, although the mesh side panels were retained. The changes to the bonnet were overshadowed by the addition of a new cab – the OPU. The Operator Protection Unit was built at Sekura's Danish and British factories and shipped to the assembly line at Mannheim.

The Sekura cab was a pleasant place to be and was rated at 84dB, whilst offering good all-round visibility. It would never set the farming world alight like Ford's Q-cab or the International Harvester/Porsche XL unit, but was a good bridge between the Duncan unit that preceded it and the remarkable in-house SG2 that would follow on later models.

The new tractor was also available with four-wheel drive as an option – which really helped to put the power down on the ground. The 6329D was a good engine, but in the hands of an experienced operator – who wasn't used to its characteristics – its short stroke occasionally let it down when the going got really tough. This is where the extra traction from a powered front axle helped.

Having said this, the 3130 was a good tractor for undertaking primary cultivation work, mainly because of its hydraulic system. It had an accurate, lower-link sensed system that was perfect for inching the plough out of the ground when a tough patch was encountered. The tractor also found favour with contractors who liked plenty of power at the pto for hedgecutters and large flails. Excellent manoeuvrability made the two-wheel drive version the perfect machine for such jobs.

The 3130 wasn't the fastest tractor on the road, by any means, but hauling loaded wheat trailers to the grain store wasn't a problem with over 90hp at the driver's disposal, a pick-up hitch and the synchromesh gearbox.

All in all, the 3130 was one of the tractors that helped John Deere to gain a foothold in Europe – and Britain in particular. It paved the way for the six-cylinder tractors that are now the mainstay of the company's sales and provided a reliable platform on which a valuable reputation could be built. ∎

> Even the exhaust system was a work of art – with the manifold more akin to a sculpture and an oval-shaped, matt-black silencer crowning the bonnet

Technical specification

Produced:	1972-1979
Engine:	John Deere 6329D
Cylinders:	6
Bore x stroke:	4.02in x 4.33in
Displacement:	329cu in
Torque:	New Gen.: 229lb ft @1,210rpm
	Gen. II: 218lb ft @1,300rpm
Horsepower:	New Gen.: 89hp
	Gen. II: 92hp
Transmission:	12 forward, 6 reverse
Speed range:	NG.: 1.2mph – 15.3mph
	G.II: 1.4mph – 17.6mph
Linkage:	Category II
Lift capacity:	New Gen.; 7,452lbs
	Gen. II: 7,496lbs
Weight:	New Gen.: 8,984lbs
	Gen. II 2WD: 9,436lbs
	Gen. II 4WD: 9,899lbs
Tyre sizes:	NG.: Front: 7.50x18
	Rear: 18.4x34
	G.II 2WD: Front: 7.50x20
	Rear: 16.9x38
	G.II 4WD: Front: 12.4x24
	Rear: 16.9x38

The tractor has completed in excess of 8,000 hours with regular servicing the only work carried out on it. Photo: Scott Lambert

The Massey Ferguson 1200 is equally suited to both three-point linkage and drawbar work. Photo: Peter D Simpson

Massey Ferguson 1200

Manchester, UK: 1972-1979

Of all the tractors that captured the minds of young boys in the 1970s, the MF 1200 was surely the most memorable. Perhaps it was the four equal-sized wheels, or maybe the bright red livery – but with that pivot in the middle, it just looked like good fun to drive!

It turns out that those boys were right – it was a brilliant tractor that encompassed all that was good about Massey Ferguson tractors of the period; a well-proven engine, useful transmission and excellent hydraulic

system. It was just what farmers on large arable farms had been waiting for.

The tractor was quite unlike anything seen in Britain before – Doe's Triple-D had made its mark on bigger farms, and pictures of the big tractors used by our Stateside cousins had seen the light of day in *Farmers' Weekly* – but the 1200 was a true revelation.

At first glance it looked a little front heavy, as the engine, transmission and cab were all positioned on the front portion, whilst the hydraulics, pto and three-point linkage were situated on the rear segment. There was method behind the MF engineers' madness, in that although

the nose heavy front-end handled 68 per cent of the machine's total weight, equilibrium was restored when a mounted implement was put into work. This action produced true 50:50 weight distribution with perfect traction for each wheel.

As was the design ethic with the vast majority of Massey Ferguson tractors of the time, keeping the weight down was imperative – whilst enabling the tractor to share the load, create additional traction and remain highly-manoeuvrable at the headland. With the pivot point allowing 42 degrees of movement in either direction, an impressive turning radius of 12 feet was achievable – not radically different to MF's two-wheel drive machines. The fulcrum also enabled the rear segment to oscillate 15 degrees either side of centre so that all four wheels were on the ground, even in more undulating conditions.

Inside, the 1200 was pure British Massey Ferguson too, with the familiar dials and controls falling easily to hand and good visibility thanks to the large expanses of glass. The superb hydraulics and Multi-

Perhaps it was the four equal-sized wheels, or maybe the bright red livery – but with that pivot in the middle, it just looked like good fun to drive!

Technical specification

Produced:	1972-1979
Engine:	Perkins A6.354
Cylinders:	6
Bore x stroke:	3.9in x 5.0in
Displacement:	354cu in
Torque:	264lb ft @1,400rpm
Horsepower:	105hp
Transmission:	12 forward, 4 reverse
Speed range:	1.2mph – 17.4mph
Linkage:	Category II
Lift capacity:	7,496lbs
Weight:	11,367lbs
Tyre sizes:	Front: 12.8x38
	Rear: 12.8x38

Power transmission gave the operator the versatility to cope with any type of work – something not offered by the larger American four-wheel drive tractors. The 1200 was good for heavy cultivation work – salesmen regularly tried to sell MF's Huard-based four-furrow reversible plough or a chisel plough, with the tractor as a package – but was equally at home on light top work, such as rolling. The high top speed also made it useful on trailer duties, but with two pivot points – trying to reverse into the shed was made to look difficult by inexperienced drivers!

The 1200 enjoyed a good production run, with relatively few problems arising, but it was eventually succeeded by the 1250 in 1980. The new model was also built at Massey Ferguson's Barton Dock Road site, alongside some of the company's construction equipment, and was essentially the same tractor – but offered an extra seven horsepower, improved lift capacity, better steering and a heavy-duty clutch, whilst sporting different decals to its predecessor. ■

The MF 1250 (left) and 1200 models had the ability to articulate 42° in either direction. Photo: Peter D Simpson

Like all Muir-Hills, the 121 is a striking machine that is very different to the tractor with which it shares components. Photo: Chris Jaworski

Muir-Hill 121

Gloucester, UK: 1972-1982

Muir-Hill's iconic Ford 5000-based, 101 tractor had been in production for six years when its replacement, the Series II 121, was introduced to British farmers. It retained many of its predecessor's best assets, such as the highly-regarded Ford 2715E and gearbox combination, whilst offering a new flat-floor cab and larger fuel tank.

The new sliding door cab was a marked improvement on the 101's 'bean can' construction – as it was mounted on rubber pads to decrease the amount of noise and vibration emanating from the engine and transmission. Despite a very steep climb up into the high cab, access was streets ahead of the 101 and the operator had more than enough room for his lunch bag and flask, as well as having a commanding all-round view!

The 121 was direct competition for the likes of the 2715E-engined Roadless Ploughmaster 120 and County's 1164, but had more power and a tighter turning circle which, at 31ft, was an added bonus at the headland.

Much like the competition, the 121 was based predominantly on Ford parts, but had several in-house components that set it apart from the competition. The key part of the puzzle was the over-engineered transfer box – which enabled a specially-designed front axle to fit under the engine and therefore improve the turning circle. The main drawback of this design is that some of the engine's power was lost through the transfer box – about 30hp – a quarter of the Series II's output!

Like most components of this nature, the transfer box was all well and good until something went wrong – when it became an expensive, but necessary, piece of equipment to repair – but, as with all agricultural machines, it was a case of look after the machine and it'll look after you.

At the back, the hydraulics and linkage were also pure Ford – coming from the respective base model – meaning that they were well designed but often under strain. Operators assumed that as the 121 had a gutsy six-cylinder engine up front, it had the capability to utilise bigger and bigger implements – but it often didn't have the capacity to lift them. Later models had an assistor ram, which helped matters significantly.

The Series III range of 1978 took the model to unprecedented heights, with increased comfort levels in the form of the new Spacecab – a slightly larger cab that benefited from improved noise insulation and a roof-mounted air filtration unit. The operator also had the added advantage of more power, thanks to the six-cylinder unit being uprated to 132hp. The popular Dual Power transmission became an option, as the Ford 5000 gearbox was substituted for the 7600's with the arrival of the Series III, bringing with it the added advantage of a dual-speed pto.

As with all Muir-Hill tractors, the attraction appears to be their superior front axle design in comparison to their rivals – and the simple fact that they are different to other Ford derivatives. The County and Roadless machines that the Muir-Hill was pitted against in its heyday will probably continue to demand a premium over their yellow rival, but the 121 is still a very competent machine that is now becoming a common sight on the rally circuit, as well as being a cheap source of second-hand power on farms across Britain. ∎

The three-point linkage on Peter Ellis's M-H 121 is equipped with an assistor ram. Photo: Chris Jaworski

The M-H 121 used the same engine as the Roadless Ploughmaster 120 and County 1164. Photo: Chris Jaworski

Technical specification

Produced:	1972-1982
Engine:	Ford 2715E
Cylinders:	6
Bore x stroke:	4.22in x 4.52in
Displacement:	380cu in
Torque:	280lb ft @1,600rpm
Horsepower:	120hp
	Series III models uprated to 132hp
Transmission:	8 forward, 2 reverse
	doubled with Dual Power
Speed range:	1.8mph – 19.1mph
Linkage:	Category II
Lift capacity:	9,392lbs
Weight:	10,700lbs
Tyre sizes:	Front: 13.6x38
	Rear: 13.6x38

Ray Stokes traversing some undulating ground on his MF 134C. Photo: Steve Wright

Massey Ferguson 134C

Fabbrico, Italy: 1973-1979

lthough not common in Great Britain, Massey Ferguson's range of crawlers proved to be very popular in other countries and a useful addition to the company's machinery range. MF's acquisition of Landini in 1960 meant that the Italian-built crawlers could be re-badged as Massey Ferguson models, albeit with a few tweaks here and there.

Initially, there were three models in the range – the 134C, 154C and 174C – that were available in narrow, standard and wide track versions, but these were joined later by the 73hp 184C. The 44.5hp 134C was a popular machine, just as the 135 was the best-selling wheeled tractor of its horsepower class. In fact, at first glance, you'd be forgiven for thinking that the 134C was purely a tracked equivalent of the 135! In reality, virtually the only things the two had in common were the traditional red

and grey livery and the Perkins AD3.152 engine that lurked under the bonnet.

The 134C's unique selling point was that despite its small size, it was often classed as being more versatile than the high-horsepower crawlers offered by other manufacturers. This was down to the hydraulic system that was housed underneath the operator's seat. Although a small number of Massey Ferguson's new range of crawlers were produced solely with a drawbar, most farmers chose to capitalise by ordering the optional three-point linkage, with position and draft control.

This feature made the 134C popular on the continent with owners of orchards and vineyards, but some British hill farmers found the crawler to be a useful addition to their working fleets. A few were pressed into use in market garden environments, nurseries and the like where their low ground pressure was favoured when preparing seed beds, but compact Japanese

No matter what the plough, the MF 134C's track size allowed it to plough in the furrow. Photo: Steve Wright

Technical specification

Produced:	1973-1979
Engine:	Perkins AD3.152
Cylinders:	3
Bore x stroke:	3.6in x 5in
Displacement:	152.6cu in
Torque:	119lb ft @1,300rpm
Horsepower:	44.5hp
Transmission:	8 forward, 2 reverse
Speed range:	0.8mph – 6.9mph
Linkage:	Category I
Lift capacity:	5,071lbs
Weight:	5,573lbs
Track sizes:	11in or 12in

– offering eight forward speeds and two reverse. As with most crawlers, a hand-operated clutch was standard fare, with left and right foot brakes and hand-operated steering clutches. A two-speed pto was available as an option, along with a belt pulley, but these were rarely specified as belt-driven equipment was becoming less commonplace in the 1970s. Other useful options included wider track shoes, 'street pads' and front 'suitcase-style' weights.

The 134C, although perhaps not as good looking as its wheeled cousin, the 135, was still a handsome machine with pure Seventies styling. It is perhaps a shame that Massey Ferguson chose not to use the same bonnet as the 135 to provide a more unified feel, particularly as they shared the same engine, but this is a minor blemish on what was a useful machine in all respects.

A small number of 134Cs appear on the rally circuit, but many can still be found at work on the Italian hillsides and in the vineyards of France, where their good build quality and excellent reliability make them firm favourites with their owners. ∎

Bill Stokes using the MF 134C with a two-furrow Ferguson plough. Photo: Steve Wright

tractors had, in the main, already begun to establish themselves in such places.

In the past, crawlers were largely consigned to heavy drawbar work with disc harrows and sub-soilers, but the addition of a tool carrier enabled them to use mounted ploughs – previously the domain of wheeled tractors. Some manufacturers offered three-point linkages on their tracked machines, as was the case with the IH BTD-6, but these were few and far between. Those farmers that did plough with their crawler were confined to ploughing 'on the land', as the tracks were too wide to plough in the furrow – but the 134C changed this. A standard track width of 11in meant that the little MF could plough just like its wheeled counterpart, with the added benefit of being able to lift the plough hydraulically at the headland.

An independent pto was standard equipment, along with a swinging drawbar, track guards and a dual-range transmission

Zetor Crystal 12011/12045

Brno, Czechoslovakia: 1974-1984

Back in the mid-Seventies there was a viable alternative to the high-horsepower, two-wheel drive machines offered by the big manufacturers: it was the Czechoslovakian-built Zetor 12011. At a time when Ford was selling the 110hp 8600 and 135hp 9600 models and Massey Ferguson was offering the 121hp 1135, Zetor was producing the 12011 for much less money whilst providing operators with a high-spec machine.

The 12011's production life started with the introduction of the second Unified Range (UR2) of tractors, dubbed the Crystal. Zetor decided that its existing tractors were too small for the ever-expanding arable farms in Europe and introduced the 8011 and 8045 models in 1970 to appeal to owners of such farms, whilst the bigger 12011 model emerged in 1974.

The first thing to note about this tractor is that it featured the world's first safety cab, mounted on rubber blocks to reduce noise and vibration. It was also the first

tractor cab to meet the stringent 85dB noise level demands in 1972. With plenty of room for the operator, a flat deck, column-mounted gear change and power steering, the Crystal's cab really was a nice place to be. It's fair to say that the cab was way ahead of its time, but was dismissed by other manufacturers as a bit of a gimmick. Of course, where one manufacturer leads, others inevitably follow and it wasn't long before all cabs were like Zetor's.

Under the cab was a well-engineered gearbox and back axle – one that could withstand the rigours of heavy implements and over-zealous operators. Also at the back was the in-house-devised Zetormatic system – a lower-link-sensed hydraulic system that was perfect for ploughing or cultivating, with an adequate lift capacity of 7,496lbs. The link arms were also telescopic, another helpful addition when hitching up the plough.

The Z8601 engine was perhaps the most-liked part of the tractor, in that it

... it had fantastic stamina, was pretty frugal and made a rather nice noise!

Technical specification

Produced:	1974-1984
Engine:	Zetor Z8601
Cylinders:	6
Bore x stroke:	4.33in x 4.72in
Displacement:	417.5cu in
Torque:	276lb ft @1,500rpm
Horsepower:	120hp
Transmission:	16 forward, 8 reverse
Speed range:	0.35mph – 15.84mph
Linkage:	Category II
Lift capacity:	7,496lbs
Weight:	9,039lbs
Tyre sizes:	Front: 9.00x16
	Rear: 18.4x34

The Daly family use their 1980 model on their Co Offaly farm, where its six-cylinder engine is particularly useful for pto-driven implements. Photo: Peter D Simpson

8011 to the six-cylinder, turbocharged 16045. They were well-liked by farmers because they were well-built, easy to maintain and economical, whilst offering a high level of specification at a bargain price. Any negative thoughts that farmers or the Press may have had about Zetor tractors were banished with the arrival of the Crystal – with the 12011 in particular helping the company become a force to be reckoned with in the 100hp+ sector.

Of course, the Crystal's popularity would eventually decline – as rival manufacturers' models became more and more advanced – but by that time, the 12011 had established itself. High-spec features, such as air braking, once only seen on Zetors, were now common on other tractors, swinging the balance of power back towards Ford and MF. ■

had fantastic stamina, was pretty frugal and made a rather nice noise! When coupled to the sixteen-forward, eight-reverse speed transmission, the operator had more than enough power on tap to tackle the big jobs around the farm, but was aided further by the splitter gearbox. This 'Torque Multiplier' system gave a 34 per cent reduction in speed and produced an extra barrage of pull, which was useful when undertaking demanding draft work.

The 12011 was a good tractor for most jobs, particularly for farmers who operated power-sapping trailed forage harvesters, but its four-wheel drive brother added another dimension. The 12045 had mechanical front-wheel drive and really looked the part, as well as being a good performer. It had a turning circle of just under 40 feet – certainly not the worst performer on the market at the time – and a small price to pay for the added traction that it offered over the 2WD model.

Seven models of Crystal were available, from the four-cylinder, naturally-aspirated

Although this tractor is actually a 12111 model, it is essentially a 12011 with a revised livery. Photo: Peter D Simpson

In reality the purr was more of a rugged bark, accompanied by copious amounts of turbo-whistle when under load

Looks can be deceiving – under the bonnet of Paul Tofield's 7700 lurks a turbocharged Ford four-cylinder diesel. Photo: Paul Tofield

Ford 7700

Basildon, UK & Antwerp, Belgium: 1975-1981

The first thing to say about the Ford 7700 is that it is the perfect example of the old proverb, in that you should never judge a book by its cover. When you first look at the tractor, with its prominent silencer and air pre-cleaner, you can almost hear the throaty purr of a Ford straight-six under the bonnet – but looks can be deceiving!

In reality the purr was more of a rugged bark, accompanied by copious amounts of turbo-whistle when under load. This came from a turbocharged four-cylinder Ford diesel. The early tractors used a 4.19 litre unit, while later machines utilised the Power Plus engine of 4.4in 'square' design with a displacement of 4.4 litres.

It looked particularly purposeful as the front axle was set well forward in comparison to other machines. The front portion of the

axle carrier was bolted as far forward as possible – where the weight frame would usually be bolted. This meant that the weight frame had to be of u-shaped construction, bolted to the side of the 'tombstone'.

Although not the most popular Ford tractor of the period, largely due to its price tag, the 7700 was perfect for farmers who were looking for that little something extra. The 7600 was extremely popular, but with 79hp on tap it could be a little short of grunt on demanding tasks – this is where the 7700 stepped in. It was ideally suited to ploughing with a three-furrow reversible plough, although many farmers found that it was more than capable of handling a four-furrow plough in lighter soils. It was also a handy tractor to have when preparing seedbeds, as adequate power at the shaft meant that 7700 was more than boss of a power harrow.

Heavy implements were never a problem for the tractor, with an assistor ram providing extra lift and telescopic lower-link ends making hitching a breeze. A pick-up hitch and swinging drawbar were standard, along with twin spool valves – perfect for either folding Cambridge rolls or a 10-ton trailer with hydraulic tailgate.

A synchromesh transmission meant that the tractor was excellent on the road, while the Dual Power 'splitter' made all the difference when ploughing through tough patches. Some two-wheel drive tractors were retro-fitted with Schindler front axles by dealers in the early years of the 7700, but it was Ford's, Antwerp-built, four-wheel drive model that would become the most popular. This was available to farmers from 1977 and utilised a ZF axle and 13.6x24 tyres. It, of course, gave the tractor the ability to work in even more arduous conditions than its two-wheel drive counterpart, making it a firm favourite with owners of large arable farms.

Spending many hours in the seat meant that the operator required a comfortable environment – and the tractor certainly delivered in this department. The flat-floor Q-cab was introduced prior to the 7700's launch, but was still at the forefront of cab design – providing excellent visibility and low noise levels. The Bostrom seat was excellent, the controls fell easily to hand and air conditioning was available as an option.

Perhaps the only point to note was that the interior wasn't to everyone's

Matthew Shute's 7700 received a four-wheel drive conversion later in its life. Photo: Joseph Lewis

taste. Besides the rubber floor mat, black steering wheel and dash panel, almost all of the remainder of the cab was blue. Other manufacturers had begun to take note of operator well-being and were offering interiors that were more akin to a car – but this is a minor failing.

Although not as common as its smaller siblings, the Ford 7700 can still be found hard at work on farms across Britain. Its rugged simplicity and good availability of parts make it a hit with those looking for a

cheap source of second-hand power, while those tractors that cannot find a home are popular contenders for the export market to Eastern Europe and beyond. ∎

The dash panel was clear, concise and well laid out. Photo: Paul Tofield

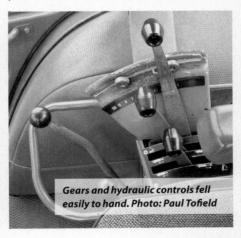

Gears and hydraulic controls fell easily to hand. Photo: Paul Tofield

A pick-up hitch and an assistor ram were standard. Photo: Paul Tofield

The 7700 had a Ford badge, rather than a blue oval. Photo: Paul Tofield

Technical specification

Produced:	1975-1981
Engine:	Ford 256DFT
	Ford Power Plus
Cylinders:	4 (turbocharged)
Bore x stroke:	4.4in x 4.2in
	4.4in x 4.4in
Displacement:	256cu in
	268cu in
Torque:	266lb ft @1,400rpm
	Unknown
Horsepower:	92hp
	94hp
Transmission:	16 forward, 4 reverse
Speed range:	1.4mph – 18.6mph
Linkage:	Category II
Lift capacity:	9,392lbs
Weight:	2WD: 9,050lbs
	4WD: 9,778lbs
Tyre sizes:	2WD: Front: 11x16
	Rear: 16.9x38
	4WD: Front: 13.6x24
	Rear: 16.9x38

FORD & Fordson TRACTORS

A bi-monthly magazine packed with the latest:

- **News**
- **Features**
- **Technical advice**
- **Tractors for sale**

For membership and subscription enquiries tel: 01959 541444

The official magazine of the Ford & Fordson Association

Early MF 590s had a two-tone, single-door cab, while later models had a two-door largely-red version. Photo: Chris McCullough

Massey Ferguson 590

Beauvais, France & Coventry, UK: 1976-1982

The Massey Ferguson 500 series – the tractors that defined agricultural machinery in the 1970s. A bold statement that's for sure, but look at the features; a good engine with a fine pedigree, all-new ergonomic cab and tried-and-tested hydraulic system – what more could a farmer want?

Massey Ferguson was keen to capitalise on the success of the outgoing 100 Series

tractors and so its designers faced a tough task when developing the new range. At the front Perkins engines were the obvious choice for power, with the engine shrouded by a square-cut bonnet that was also home to the battery, air cleaner and cab air filter. The 590's engine was rated at 75hp, putting out 67.7hp at the pto. This made it the second largest and one of the most popular in the range, 13hp adrift of the 595 – which, incidentally, was launched two years before the 550, 565, 575 and 590.

The standard transmission was a synchro unit that was either of Porsche or ZF design and provided the operator with a well-spaced range of speeds for both field and road work. It had a similar layout to its predecessor, with a long lever controlling the gears and a stubby lever flicking between high and low range. Some problems occurred with the build quality of the Porsche transmission, but as many had come to expect, the ZF unit was second-to-none.

A Multi-Power gearbox was also available that provided a change-on-the-move, clutchless shift with 12 forward and 4 reverse speeds – but, as we all know, there was no engine braking in low and the tractor couldn't be bump-started.

The hydraulic controls were perhaps the oldest technology on the 590, as they were pure Ferguson system with two levers providing draft and position control. This was not particularly advanced but was simple and effective – and as the old ➡

saying goes; 'If it ain't broke, don't fix it'! An assistor ram helped to push the lift capacity of the category II linkage to 5,818lbs – a useful addition when working with the heavy reversible ploughs that were now the vogue. A drawbar was standard, but the 500 Series' launch coincided with the transition from drawbars to pick-up hitches and so later 590s have an added string to their bow.

To be honest, these other features were all well and good, but the one component

that truly set the tractor apart from its rivals – and the one that made it the icon it is today – is the cab. Massey Ferguson, aware of impending changes to the legislation regarding noise levels, was keen to stay ahead of the game and commissioned Sankey to design a flat-floor cab with noise levels not exceeding 85dB at the operator's ear. If truth be told, it was this change in legislation that heralded the arrival of the 590 and its stablemates, as

it was deemed too expensive to design a new cab that would be suitable for all of the models in the ageing 100 Series.

The 590's cab is still good today, but back then it was brilliant! Only in recent years have manufacturers begun to offer four-post cabs on their tractors, with many being of the six-post variety, but Sankey managed to produce a design that offered safety, good visibility, ergonomically-driven styling and unhindered access – in 1976! Some

> ... Sankey managed to produce a design that offered safety, good visibility, ergonomically-driven styling and unhindered access – in 1976!

Trevor Chippendale's French-built 4WD model with Multi-Power transmission. Photo: Lorraine Chippendale

This immaculate MF 590 is owned by MF dealer John McElderry of Ballymoney, Northern Ireland. Photo: Chris McCullough

operators criticised the fact that the cab only had one door and so this was rectified with the launch of the two-door version in 1979 – at last, everyone was happy!

With plenty of power on tap the 590 was never really strained, except when in the hands of an over-zealous operator, but the introduction of four-wheel drive in 1978 was a welcome option. These new tractors were built at the Beauvais factory in France, along with a four-wheel drive version of the 575. Production of these models was confined to Beauvais, whilst their two-wheel drive siblings continued to be built in France and at Banner Lane, Coventry – depending on their specification. A two-wheel drive 590 could cope admirably with MF's 52 model trailed disc harrow or the Huard-derived three-furrow reversible plough in most soil conditions. But in really heavy soils four-wheel drive was the only option.

The Massey Ferguson 590 would have once been the prime mover on many farms across Europe, but will have now been either traded in for a newer model or relegated to secondary operations, such as hedge trimming or yard scraping. In two-wheel drive configuration the 590 is the perfect machine for small baling and trailer operations, whilst the four-wheel drive version is still adequate for providing primary cultivation duties on small-acreage farms. With many 590s being retired from frontline duties, collectors of classic tractors are snapping them up – as parts are readily available. They are straightforward to work on and

restored examples always capture people's imagination on the rally circuit. Quite simply, the MF 500 Series – and the 590 in particular – will always be an icon of the '70s. ■

Technical specification

Produced:	1976-1982
Engine:	Perkins A4.248S
Cylinders:	4
Bore x stroke:	3.975in x 5in
Displacement:	248cu in
Torque:	202.5lb ft @1,400rpm
Horsepower:	75hp
Transmission:	8 forward, 2 reverse
	12 forward, 4 reverse (Multi-Power)
Speed range:	1.6mph – 18.2mph
	1.2mph – 19.4mph (Multi-Power)
Linkage:	Category II
Lift capacity:	4,900lbs
Weight:	10,700lbs
Tyre sizes:	2WD: Front: 7.50x16
	Rear: 16.9x34
	4WD: Front: 10x24
	Rear: 12x38

Mike Scaife owns this lovely example of a Ford FW-30. Photo: Peter D Simpson

Ford FW-30

Fargo, North Dakota, USA: 1977-1982

The FW Series tractors were green giants in disguise. They were built by Steiger in North Dakota, at the Fargo facility, and closely resembled the Series III Panther tractors – but were produced to Ford's exacting specifications. The agreement between the two companies enabled Steiger's product to reach a worldwide audience, via Ford's extensive dealer network, albeit in a blue and white livery.

The tractors had built a good reputation in America for their traction and drawbar abilities and Ford was keen to use this to its advantage. Min-til was on the increase and bigger tractors were needed to pull heavier implements across wider fields – so the four-wheel drive (FW) series was perfect for the job. The articulated giants also had another ace up their sleeve – the engine. Interestingly, of the 50 tractors assembled here, the FW-30 is the only one that features a V8 engine – and some engine it was too. The Cummins power plant churned out a respectable

265hp, but this was often increased with a slight tweak to the fuel pump.

The FW-30 was launched in 1978 but would be joined two years later by the 335hp flagship FW-60, whilst completing the line-up were the FW-20 and FW-40 models. All of the tractors, with the exception of the turbocharged FW-60, used naturally-aspirated Cummins V8 engines. The FW-40 was discontinued in 1980, with many FW-30s having their injectors adjusted to equal the output of the bigger model. Of course, many farmers retro-fitted turbochargers and tweaked fuel pumps to uprate their FW-30s, with many pushing the horsepower rating beyond the 300hp mark.

The transmission on the FW-30 was a Spicer, 10 forward, 2 reverse unit that could be doubled with the optional two-speed transfer case. This channelled the power to the Steiger-Raba axles that

The centre pivot-steer concept was pioneered by Steiger in the early 1960s. Photo: Peter D Simpson

featured automatic diff locks and planetary reduction gears at each end to reduce drivetrain torque. Putting the power down was never really a problem for the FW-30, as it weighed in at a colossal 31,310lbs – an added bonus when pulling a tillage train.

As the FW-30 was predominantly built for drawbar work, those that were sold outside Britain had four spool valves for slave cylinders, but didn't feature a three-point linkage. The majority of UK-spec machines featured a hefty, category III linkage, capable of lifting a respectable

12,000lbs, while some also had the optional pto pack. This was a hydraulically-driven unit that offered both 540rpm and 1,000rpm speeds – but suffered in that it could only muster about 55hp in 540rpm mode and just over 100hp in 1,000rpm mode. Few farmers needed pto capability from such a machine and so this was never really a concern.

The FW-30's pièce de résistance was its spacious and comfortable cab. Ford opted to retain the Steiger unit, which is no great surprise when you look inside. It featured all the mod-cons of the

day; sound insulation, stereo radio, air conditioning and tinted glass. All controls fell easily to hand, the pedals were light to depress and the adjustable steering wheel provided a positive and easy response.

The FW-30 was a well-liked machine that justified its £40,000 price tag, with many continuing to see service across the world. It is popular with farmers looking for a cheap source of second-hand power as it is reliable, whilst being well-built and capable of most primary tillage jobs on large-acreage farms. ■

Dials and switches were easy to read, with all controls falling easily to hand. Photo: Howard Sherren

Technical specification

Produced:	1977-1982
Engine:	Cummins V-903
Cylinders:	8
Bore x stroke:	5.50in x 4.75in
Displacement:	903cu in
Torque:	657lb ft @1,500rpm
Horsepower:	265hp
Transmission:	10 forward, 2 reverse or 20 forward, 4 reverse
Speed range:	2.1mph – 21.6mph
Linkage:	Category III
Lift capacity:	12,000lbs
Weight:	31,310lbs
Tyre sizes:	Front: 18.4x34 or 24.5x32 Rear: 18.4x34 or 24.5x32

… there aren't many tractors that sound better than a D-358-powered International in full flow!

International Harvester 955

St Dizier, France, & Neuss, Germany: 1977-1981

I t's difficult to say how well-loved the IH 955 was, and still is, by European farmers – it proved to be a winner for International Harvester and helped to cement the company as one of the leading tractor manufacturers. It was part of International Harvester's Hi-Performers range of European-built tractors – introduced to dealers in 1977 – and a far cry from the 45hp 384 model built in Britain.

At a time when the likes of the John Deere 3130, Massey Ferguson 595 and the Ford 7700 were taking command in the 90hp sector, IH knew that it had

to produce a special tractor to win over farmers. All of this was happening when the transition from two-wheel to four-wheel drive was taking place and so the new tractor would have to be designed to work well in either configuration. As fate would have it, IH could have attached four wheelbarrow wheels to the engine and operators would have still loved it!

The heart of any tractor is the engine, but the 955's was very special indeed. The first incarnation of the tractor was fitted with the D-310 six-cylinder unit and this proved to be very popular, but the machine would be improved further still with the introduction of the D-358 engine

in July 1979. This powerplant is the stuff of legends – it's long stroke providing tremendous lugging power without the 'shouting' that was associated with some of the other manufacturers' engines.

Some decided that four cylinders were more than adequate for generating 90hp, while some added a turbocharger to give that extra grunt. IH and John Deere both opted for a naturally-aspirated six-cylinder engine, but the Deere's shorter stroke meant it was prone to dying under heavy load. International Harvester had always been known for its lugging engines and the D-358 was no exception. It was a much better unit than the out-going D-310 and gave the later incarnations of the 955 the edge over the competition.

The D-358 used in the 955 was a de-rated version of the engine used in the 1055 and the turbocharged 1255 and is famed for its characteristic exhaust note – there aren't many tractors that sound better than a D-358-powered International in full flow!

Although the engine is the element that the 955 is most famed for, the cab played a major role in winning over farmers. The

vast majority of tractors were turned out with either a Fritzmeier or Timmerman cab, depending on where they were built. The British-specification tractors, built at the St Dizier plant in France, were all fitted with the Timmerman Super Comfort 2000 – a flat-decked unit with tinted glass.

The IH 955 was always a great tractor, but it became an outstanding tractor in 1981, when it was developed into the 955XL. The Porsche-designed XL cab was a revelation – a trendsetter in so many ways. It was the best available at the time and IH was so pleased with the advance over previous designs that it no longer deemed it to be a cab – it was now dubbed the operator control centre. Whereas the Timmerman had a gear lever either side of the seat, the French-built XL had everything, with the exception of the handbrake, positioned to the driver's right-hand side. Add superb visibility, good ventilation, a suspension seat and stereo audio to the equation and it becomes evident what a nice place it was in which to spend long working hours.

It was always intended that the 955 would be a good all-rounder and so four-wheel

drive had to be an option. ZF provided the necessary hardware to turn the tractor from an excellent, two-wheel drive, grassland tractor into an arable Colossus. With plenty of low-down torque and enough power at the pto for most applications, the standard 955 was perfect for contract mowing and forage harvesting, whilst its four-wheel drive sibling was the perfect companion for a four-furrow plough or disc harrows.

Unfortunately, in some cases, the 955 was its own worst enemy – as the gutsy nature of the engine led many operators to believe that the tractor was comfortable punching above its weight on a regular basis. An adequate lift capacity and the never-say-die engine invited many to push the 955 far beyond what it was actually designed for – resulting in the fact that many suffered a hard life with few surviving today in a tidy state.

The 955XL would, of course, eventually metamorphose into the ubiquitous 956XL – the top of many farmers' wish lists – but it was the 955 that laid the foundations for this legendary machine. A great tractor if ever there was one. ∎

Technical specification

Produced:	1977-1981
Engine:	IH D-310/D-358
Cylinders:	6
Bore x stroke:	D-310: 3.87in x 4.37in
	D-358: 3.87in x 5.06in
Displacement:	310cu in
	358cu in
Torque:	D-310: 235.28lb ft @1,500rpm
	D-358: 246.35lb ft @1,400rpm
Horsepower:	90hp
Transmission:	16 forward, 8 reverse
Speed range:	1.1mph – 17.6mph
Linkage:	Category II
Lift capacity:	9,535lbs
Weight:	2WD (D-310): 9,017lbs
	4WD (D-310): 10,108lbs
	2WD (D-358): 9,458lbs
	4WD (D-358): 10,296lbs
Tyre sizes:	Front (2WD) : 7.50x18
	Front (4WD) : 12.4x28
	Rear: 18.4x34

International Harvester 3588

Rock Island, Illinois, USA: 1979-1981

With the likes of Steiger, Versatile and the big manufacturers making in-roads into the high-horsepower, four-wheel drive sector, International Harvester was keen not to get left behind and worked hard to come up with a solution that would be useful to farmers and simple to produce as well as profitable.

IH had already toyed with big tractors in the years prior to the launch of the 3588, with the articulated 4366 model heading the range, powered by a 466cu in straight-six diesel engine, but the new tractors that it eventually produced were quite unlike anything seen before.

The 2+2 range, as it was designated, was an innovative, articulated design that relied heavily on the company having a good stock of components in its existing parts bins! IH was keen to keep costs to a minimum and so, where possible, used existing components. The back-end was pure 86 Series, utilising everything possible from the tractors that had proven their worth with farmers since 1976, including the IH Control Center. At the front, was the IH 4366's venerable DT-466 engine and, strangely enough, a British-built axle assembly.

Initially, the 3588 was the largest of the two-tractor range, the other was the 157hp 3388. Luckily for IH, the tractor proved to be immensely popular and so a third model was introduced – the 200hp 3788. It's fair to say that the 2+2 tractors were more of a hit in their homeland, where some fields were as big as entire European farms, but owners of large arable farms in Britain saw the benefits of operating such machines and bought the tractor in such numbers that International Harvester deemed it viable to continue selling them for some time. At this point it is worth mentioning that in the United States the 2+2 tractors were dubbed 'Anteaters', due to their long noses, while in Britain and many other countries the style was affectionately known as 'Snoopy'.

The long sloping bonnet hid the key to the tractor's success. The turbocharged, straight-six diesel was positioned right at the front, with the fuel tank directly above the front axle – which offered near 50:50 weight distribution to reduce soil compaction. It also provided excellent traction and ballast to compensate the use of heavy mounted implements.

The design was such that it was marketed as a dual-purpose tractor. The Control ➡

… in the United States the 2+2 tractors were dubbed 'Anteaters', due to their long noses, while in Britain and many other countries the style was affectionately known as 'Snoopy'

Technical specification

Produced:	1979-1981
Engine:	IH DT-466B
Cylinders:	6
Bore x stroke:	4.3in x 5.35in
Displacement:	466cu in
Torque:	450lb ft @1,800rpm
Horsepower:	177hp
Transmission:	16 forward, 8 reverse
Speed range:	1.8mph – 17.5mph
Linkage:	Category III
Lift capacity:	8,376lbs
Weight:	16,520lbs
Tyre sizes:	Front: 18.4x38
	Rear: 18.4x38

David and Laurence McMullan's 1981 IH 3588 was originally one of a pair imported from Canada. Photo: Chris McCullough

The 3588's back-end was pure IH 86 series, including the legendary Control Center. Photo: Peter D Simpson

Center was mounted on the rear portion of the tractor and offered an excellent view of the implement. This was perfect in the USA, where it was used extensively for row-crop operations. The beauty of such a layout, in comparison to conventional articulated models, was that the operator had near-perfect vision all around the tractor, while being able to hitch implements easily and turn sharply at the headlands – just like a two-wheel drive tractor.

The Control Center was a very nice place to be. It was fitted with plush carpets in place of rubber matting, a heavily-padded seat and air conditioning. Noise levels were kept low due to the fact that the engine was a long distance from the cab and the exhaust silencer was located under the bonnet – which also aided forward visibility. The majority of the controls were placed either side of the seat, improving access into and out of the two-door cab. The 3588 and its siblings were equipped, like most other high-powered tractors of the time, with a pto and three-point linkage as standard, while a diff-lock and four spool valves gave the driver the ability to use a wide range of implements – such as

folding disc harrow and roll combinations. A good range of field speeds was offered by the 16-forward, 8-reverse transmission, with the added benefit of IH's Torque Amplifier system – essentially a splitter.

The 2+2 concept was revamped in 1982 when IH introduced three updated models, designated the 60 Series 2+2

tractors. These were sold until 1984 when they were replaced by the 'Super 70s' – the 7288 and 7488. This pairing was extremely short-lived and was dropped when J I Case's parent company, Tenecco, purchased the agricultural equipment division of International Harvester, merging it with the Case line. ∎

With its unique articulated design, the 3588 was brilliant at the headland. Photo: Peter D Simpson

REMAN MEANS VALUE FOR MONEY

- **Manufacturer one year warranty!**
- **Environmentally friendly!**
- **Reduced downtime in the workshop!**
- **The same performance as a brand new part!**

"Remanufactured" parts are completely disassembled, cleaned and individually inspected to ensure they conform to Case IH's original specifications. Components which cannot be reconditioned to meet their original specifications are discarded.

Injection pumps and nozzles are fully disassembled, renovated and individually tested before reassembly on the engine. Electronic sub-assemblies and components are thoroughly tested using the latest software, to the same standards as original parts. Engines are assembled following the same procedures as those just off the production line. All seals, bearings, pistons, rings and sensors are replaced 100% by original parts. External engine accessories: turbochargers, oil pumps, water pumps, supply pumps are also renovated using original components. Each engine is fully tested before being dispatched for delivery.

Contact your CASE IH Dealer for more information.

www.caseih.com

CASE IH. For those who demand more.

Jamie Leigh's beautifully-restored County 1884 was one of a pair supplied new to Wallasea Farms, Essex, in 1981. Photo: Howard Sherren

County 1884

Fleet, UK: 1980-1989

During the history of County Commercial Cars, many remarkable machines were produced, but none can quite match the status enjoyed by the company's flagship model – the 1884.

Ironically, this was the last equal-size wheeled tractor that County built and, at 188hp, the largest too. Just like its predecessors, the 1884 was built following the launch of a new Ford model – in this case the brilliant TW-30. The Ford already had the credentials to make it an outstanding machine; a powerful engine, useful transmission and the now famous Q 'bubble' cab. County was able to capitalise

on this by adding its front axle technology to harness even more of the Ford's power.

It goes without saying that every great tractor revolves around a good engine, but the Ford 401cu in unit used in the 1884 was a truly exceptional powerplant. It was the same straight-six, turbocharged diesel used in the Ford TW-20, but with the help of an intercooler and a few tweaks to the fuel pump, the engine managed to push out a colossal 188hp.

The gearbox given the task of absorbing this power was Ford's Dual Power system, offering 16 forward and four reverse gears. On the TW-30 this put the power through the rear wheels via a bar-type axle, but due to the unique front axle design on the County, the wheels were bolted to fixed hubs.

At the business end of the tractor, dual assistor rams enabled the 1884 to lift in excess of six-and-a-half tons – more than enough for lifting a six-furrow fully-mounted plough. A 1,000rpm pto also featured, but with most Countys finding use on primary cultivation work, this saw precious little action. All that power on tap meant that the 1884 was a good model with which to power a trailed forage harvester, but its huge turning circle of almost 50 feet meant that it was best suited to a semi-mounted plough, in a big field where large headlands were of no real concern.

The 1884 had what it took to tame the most demanding of ground conditions and was well-liked by farmers who grew crops on steep, heavy clay-based fields. Growing potatoes requires a good seed bed and many farmers used the 1884 and a reversible plough to achieve a deep tilth. It was also popular with contractors who needed to get the job done quickly to keep costs to a minimum. Being Ford-based also helped to reduce down-time when breakdowns

Technical specification

Produced:	1980-1989
Engine:	Ford 401 DFT
Cylinders:	6
Bore x stroke:	4.4in x 4.4in
Displacement:	401cu in
Torque:	456lb ft @1,600rpm
Horsepower:	188hp
Transmission:	16 forward, 4 reverse
Speed range:	1.6mph – 19.8mph
Linkage:	Category II
Lift capacity:	14,694lbs
Weight:	17,703lbs
Tyre sizes:	Front: 18.4x38
	Rear: 18.4x38

The business end of the County 1884 – simple, but effective. Photo: Howard Sherren

occurred or servicing was required, as parts were cheap and readily available.

County was in the business of making good tractors even better with the addition of its four-wheel drive system, but as Roadless, Muir-Hill and other conversion specialists would all eventually find out, success would be short-lived. Ford was not keen to continue to lose sales and began to offer its own four-wheel drive systems that were considerably cheaper than the specialist tractors produced by County et al.

The TW range is the perfect example of this, as it was one of the factors that contributed to County's downfall. When it was launched in 1979 the range solely offered two-wheel drive machines, enabling County to buy the perfect skid unit to convert into four-wheel drive machines. No sooner had County begun producing the flagship 1884, than Ford offered the TW range with four-wheel drive – albeit in unequal-size wheel form. County continued to produce tractors and aimed its products at specialist sectors, such as airports and forestry, but its heyday was long gone and the equal-wheeled Goliaths were confined to the history books.

Many of these tractors are still hard at work and continue to attract an incredibly loyal following, with a price tag to match. The later, Super-Q-cabbed, derivatives command a particular premium, as they were built in very few numbers and add another dimension to an already great tractor. The 1884 may have been built in small numbers, but was well built and reliable – making it an attractive second-hand source of power for large-acreage farmers, as well as capturing the hearts and minds of tractor enthusiasts the world over. ∎

... it was best suited to a semi-mounted plough, in a big field where large headlands were of no real concern

Undulating ground and a seven-furrow semi-mounted plough – the perfect match for a County 1884. Photo: Howard Sherren

David Brown 1490

Meltham Mills, UK: 1980-1984

After the relative success of its previous models, David Brown was keen to offer a new design that would bring its tractors into line with the models offered by opposition manufacturers. A reliable engine, innovative gearbox and all-new styling would be the order of the day for the arrival of the new 90 Series tractors in 1980.

The 83hp 1490 was the largest four-cylinder tractor in the range and was available as either a two or four-wheel drive variant. It featured an in-house developed engine that was designed from the outset to be a turbocharged unit, with a large-diameter crankshaft, large oil galleries and

cross-flow cylinder head to provide farmers with a reliable, high-torque motor that was up to the job. David Brown was keen to emphasise the point that it was a tractor specialist and its engines were designed for tractors – and nothing else – making them some of the most economical and fit-for-purpose tractor engines on the market.

Power from the engine was channelled through one of two transmissions – either the standard synchromesh transmission or the optional Hydra-Shift unit. The 12-forward, 4-reverse standard gearbox utilised four gears in each of three forward ranges and one reverse range, with synchromesh on second and third gears.

Unlike the standard transmission, the Hydra-Shift system was only available on the two-wheel drive model and consisted of four, clutch-less change-on-the-go speeds to have two tractors for the price of one.

The flat-decked Sekura-built cab was vastly superior to its predecessor in that it had much better access – thanks to wide rear-hinged doors – and an uncluttered feel, largely attributed to the pendant-mounted pedals and saddle-mounted fuel tanks below. Tinted glass was standard and a well-laid-out central console kept the operator up-to-speed with all major functions.

Whilst the forward position of the cab helped to improve access, it also gave more clearance at the business end of the tractor. Implements could be hitched more easily and safely than ever before and an optional dual hydraulic pump and assistor ram increased lift capacity to 4,761lbs. This wasn't ground-breaking performance, but was ample for the implements that farmers would be using with the tractor and, coupled with the familiar single-lever Selectamatic hydraulic system, was ideal for primary cultivations with a three-furrow reversible plough.

A swinging drawbar was standard, but the heavy-duty pick-up hitch was a much-specified optional extra – as the 1490's synchro 'box and turbocharged engine made it a popular tractor for trailer work, particularly during the summer harvest.

The Hydra-Shift transmission made the tractor a popular choice for livestock farmers or those looking to assign a capable machine to general materials handling duties, but the 1490 managed to find favour on both arable and livestock farms of all sizes. Farmers who were staunch supporters of the marque knew what to expect from the new tractor, while others were converted after experiencing a demonstration – with the 90 Series, and the 1490 in particular, selling well until the introduction of the 94 Series in 1984. ∎

Technical specification

Produced:	1980-1984
Engine:	David Brown AD4/55T
Cylinders:	4 (turbocharged)
Bore x stroke:	3.94in x 4.5in
Displacement:	219.3cu in
Torque:	209.5lb ft @1,600rpm
Horsepower:	83hp
Transmission:	12 forward, 4 reverse
	(optional Hydra-Shift on 2WD)
Speed range:	1.2mph – 16.7mph
	1.1mph – 16mph (Hydra-Shift)
Linkage:	Category II
Lift capacity:	4,009lbs
Weight:	2WD: 7,500lbs
	4WD: 7,900lbs
Tyre sizes:	2WD: Front: 7.50x18
	Rear: 13.6x38
	4WD: Front: 11.2x24
	Rear: 16.9x34

The inherent strength of the front axle made the four-wheel drive version of the 1490 a popular choice for loader work. Photo: Kim Parks

> ... the Hydra-Shift system was only available on the two-wheel drive model and consisted of four, clutch-less change-on-the-go speeds in creep, field, road or reverse ranges

in creep, field, road or reverse ranges. The beauty of the system was that engine braking was available in every gear and during the winter months, when the battery might not have quite enough cranking power, a chain could be attached to the front axle and the tractor could be tow-started!

The Carraro-built four-wheel drive option was obviously useful for farmers that needed extra traction on wet, heavy or undulating ground, but another useful variation was available to farmers who required extra versatility when working in row-crop conditions. A high-clearance kit enabled farmers to convert their 1490 from a primary cultivation tractor to a spraying or weeding specific machine with an extra 7½in of ground clearance. This conversion could be carried out simply on the farm and enabled farmers

David Brown's turbocharged four-cylinder engine had more than enough grunt for the most demanding applications. Photo: Paul Tofield

At the heart of this fantastic package was a brilliant four-cylinder engine

John Deere 1640

Mannheim, Germany: 1980-1982

L arge-acreage farmers looking for a Jack-of-all-trades and smallholders searching for a prime mover in the early-Eighties, need have looked no further than the John Deere 1640. A lively, lightweight little number with a gutsy engine and brilliant cab, the 1640 was an operator's dream.

Many farmers reported that the 1640 was so good that it took on the role of a bigger tractor and was used for jobs far beyond what it was actually designed for. This resulted in the early demise of some machines – an unfortunate, but obvious consequence.

At the heart of this fantastic package was a brilliant four-cylinder engine that was somewhat deceptive in that it appeared to have the power and torque of a much larger tractor. John Deere was keen to over-engineer its powerplants to ensure reliability and long service, whilst opting to use larger displacements to develop sufficient power and torque without putting the unit under strain. Needless to say, because of this, operators loved the 1640's engine!

A good engine is nothing without an equally good transmission – and the little Deere didn't disappoint. The standard gearbox was the Synchron unit that provided 8 forward and 4 reverse speeds through a two-range system. The levers spouted from the transmission tunnel, between the clutch and brake pedals and so access was largely unimpeded. Selection was positive, yet smooth and Deere boasted that its system was quiet, strong and reliable – something that appears to have been true, as many John Deere 1640s are still in active service almost 30 years on, with no reported problems.

This JD 1640 belongs to Ian Butler, of Cambridgeshire, and has completed 6,800 hours with no major problems – not even a clutch replacement. Photo: Scott Lambert

The Power Synchron transmission was a nice alternative, as it provided change-on-the-move shifting by pushing either a lever on the dashboard across, or the gear lever itself across – depending on the type of cab fitted. This leads nicely to the operator's environment, as the 1640 featured two different cabs throughout its production – the OPU and SG2. The OPU, or Operator's Protection Unit, was built by Sekura in its British and Danish factories and was then shipped to be united with the skid unit on the assembly line in Mannheim.

Production of the 1640 was virtually at the mid-way point when the Sound-Gard 2 cab was introduced. Not all operators liked its quirky design, but it was largely hailed as one of the best tractor cabs on the market during its ten-year plus lifespan. The JD-designed SG2 was unique in that it had a rounded front which helped to deflect light, dust and noise away from the operator and was so good that it achieved the lowest interior sound level for any four-cylinder tractor available at the time – just 79.5dB at the driver's ear.

It also had many other excellent features, such as a fully-adjustable steering wheel – for both rake and reach, a deluxe fabric seat with lumbar support, eight adjustable air vents and console-mounted gear selection (with the exception of the budget X-E Series tractors which retained the floor-mounted gear levers and were recognisable by their yellow cab roofs).

For those that demanded four-wheel drive, the 1640 didn't disappoint. The tractor was one of a long line that would feature the innovative 'castor angle front-wheel drive' system. The ends of the front axle were sloped, allowing the front wheel to lean whilst turning – giving a phenomenal 50-degree steering angle. The mechanical front-wheel drive was also engaged or disengaged on-the-move, without declutching, via a dash-mounted rocker switch.

The castor angle steering on four-wheel drive models was a unique selling point. Photo: Scott Lambert

At the rear, ample hydraulic capacity meant that the 1640 could lift a four-furrow reversible plough with ease, whilst John Deere's Load-and-Depth Control ensured that either a constant or varying implement depth was maintained according to the operator's preference. This was adjustable, via hand control, on-the-move and worked through a lower-link sensing system.

The John Deere 1640 really was different to other tractors of the time, as it had wonderful cutting-edge looks and many innovative features that set it apart from the opposition. Although other tractors had their merits (the Massey Ferguson 565 for example) the 1640 looked and felt as though it belonged in the future – it truly was one of the nicest tractors of its generation. ∎

The business end of the JD 1640 was simple, but effective and had a lift capacity of 6,769lbs. Photo: Scott Lambert

Technical specification

Produced:	1980-1982
Engine:	John Deere 4239DL03
Cylinders:	4
Bore x stroke:	4.19in x 4.33in
Displacement:	239.2cu in
Torque:	151.2lb ft @1,200rpm
Horsepower:	62hp
Transmission:	8 forward, 4 reverse
	16 forward, 8 reverse (Power Synchron)
Speed range:	1.6mph – 18.3mph
Linkage:	Category II
Lift capacity:	6,770lbs
Weight:	2WD: 7,020lbs
	4WD: 7,650lbs
Tyre sizes:	2WD: Front: 7.50x16
	Rear: 13.6x36
	4WD: Front: 11.2x24
	Rear: 13.6x36

Marshall 802/804

Gainsborough, UK: 1980-1985

In many ways, the 802 and 804 were to Marshall what the 1490 was to David Brown. They were all four-cylinder, turbocharged tractors of roughly the same power, available in two and four-wheel drive – and to some extent even looked the same!

The Harvest Gold-liveried Marshalls were, like their David Brown nemesis, marketed as all-rounders. They appealed to farmers because they were based on a long line of Leyland tractors that were known for their simplicity, ease of maintenance and durability, but incorporated enough new features to make them an attractive proposition.

At the time of their launch, the 802 and 804 were Marshall's range-toppers – pushing out 82hp from a Leyland 4/98TT engine; the same basic unit used in the Leyland 282 Synchro. But they would later be joined by the four-cylinder 904XL and six-cylinder 100 models. The key to the tractors' success, in Marshall's eyes, was the fact that the engine had plenty of power and ample torque, whilst being fuel efficient – saving money is always popular with farmers!

The transmission was also a remnant from the Leyland days, but was a well-proven and largely-reliable gearbox. Although not ground-breaking, the shuttle transmission was dependable and won favour with the Royal Agricultural Society of England for its quality. Power was channelled through a self-adjusting 12in clutch to 9 forward and 3 reverse gears, providing a well-spaced range of speeds for field and road work – with a 20mph top speed making it particularly advantageous on trailer duties.

Whilst the two-wheel drive 802 was more suited to transport and pto work, the four-wheel drive 804 was the ideal tool for primary cultivation. Its Carraro axle gave it sufficient bite to pull through heavy land with a four-furrow reversible plough or rigid-tine cultivator in tow. Besides the shuttle facility, the tractors were also popular for loader work because of their high reverse speeds. When in third reverse gear a phenomenal top speed of 17mph could be reached!

A 55l/min capacity hydraulic pump meant that a 5,200lb lift was achievable with the standard assistor ram and two double-acting spools were fitted towards the end of production, as was a quick-hitch three-

With 82hp on tap, the Marshall 802 would have no problems powering a conventional baler. Photo: Jonathan Whitlam

Technical specification

Produced:	1980-1985
Engine:	Leyland 4/98TT
Cylinders:	4 (turbocharged)
Bore x stroke:	3.86in x 4.92in
Displacement:	230cu in
Torque:	216lb ft @1,600rpm
Horsepower:	82hp
Transmission:	9 forward, 3 reverse
Speed range:	2.2mph – 20.3mph
Linkage:	Category II
Lift capacity:	5,200lbs
Weight:	802: 6,512lbs
	804: 7,260lbs
Tyre sizes:	802: Front: 7.50x18
	Rear: 14x34
	804: Front: 11x28
	Rear: 14x34

Andrew Cook's Marshall 804 is still considered to be a useful tractor. Photo: Paul Tofield

point linkage. Draft, position and auxiliary controls fell easily to hand. A two-speed pto, controlled via an independent hand clutch, was also a standard fitment and featured interchangeable 6 and 21-spline stub shafts.

As was the case with David Brown's 90 Series tractors, the Marshalls featured a Sekura, flat-floor, Explorer cab. This had all of the bells and whistles that an operator could desire and, despite its angular appearance, complemented the curvy, Leyland-derived bonnet quite neatly. Marshall was justifiably proud of the cab and drivers commented on ease of access, ergonomic controls, low vibration levels, as well as less-significant features such as the radio/cassette player and detachable toolbox.

The Marshall 802 and 804 used their heritage to good advantage – as farmers wanted familiar technology, coupled with innovative features and a name that they could trust – after all, Marshall was a name that conjured up images of reliable single-cylinder tractors and some of the best tracklayers ever built. The duo would never set the farming world alight, but were solid and dependable machines that were cheap to run and easy to maintain – two of the most important features in a thrifty farmer's eyes. ∎

Post-1980

As tractor technology progresses at an astonishing rate, it is easy to lose sight of when certain models were first launched. We thought it would be a good idea to take a look at the tractors that emerged in the first half of the 1980s – machines that didn't quite make it into this book.

Fiatagri 90-90

As you would expect, cabs were a significant part of tractor design in the 1980s – as manufacturers understood that operator comfort was of paramount importance, with the engine performance and transmission no longer being the major design parameters.

The Fiatagri cab was designed by legendary styling house Pininfarina and offered a low noise level and well-laid-out controls. It was perhaps let down by the horizontal bar that split the windscreen at bonnet level, but operators were largely forgiving due to the tractor's performance.

Unusually, the 90-90 used a five-cylinder powerplant that was described as being like a symphony when under load. Many farmers commented that it was nice to have the radio off and the sunroof open to hear the engine in full song!

The combination of engine, ample lift capacity and compact wheelbase made the 90-90 a viable alternative to the models offered by Ford, International Harvester and John Deere. It was mostly seen in four-wheel drive configuration, but a two-wheel drive option was available until production was terminated in 1991.

International Harvester 1056XL

No matter where your allegiances lie, it's unlikely that you could fail to be impressed by the six-cylinder IH 1056XL. Its naturally-aspirated 105hp engine was renowned for its 'whistle', despite the lack of a turbocharger, and the torque generated was phenomenal.

The 1056XL's predecessor, the 955, features in this book – so it is unnecessary to go into detail about the tractor's pedigree – but the introduction of the XL unit took International Harvester to the forefront of cab technology. With help from Porsche, the cab became *the* place in which to do a hard day's work and helped propel the tractor to legendary status.

From its launch in 1982, the 1056XL was famed for its ploughing ability, largely thanks to its long-stroke engine and Sens-O-Draulic lower-link sensed hydraulic system, with farmers waxing lyrical about how the tractor constantly punched above its weight. It was continually updated, with the introduction of a 40km/h transmission and a livery change after the company became Case IH, but was so well-liked that production continued until 1992.

Massey Ferguson 230/240

It is unusual that a small tractor should feature among a group of high-horsepower machines, but the MF 230 and 240 models were considered exceptional little workhorses during the 1980s. The 240 was introduced in 1980 and was a direct descendant of the legendary 135, with the 230 following in 1983 – essentially a de-rated 240, hence the inclusion of both models here.

John Redfern's lovely 1984 IH 1056XL is completely original. Photo: Peter D Simpson

The tractors used the proven Perkins AD3.152 engine, as used in the 135, along with an eight-by-two transmission that put the power down through a traditional two-wheel drive arrangement. While the 240 produced 47hp at 2,250rpm, the 230 only managed 38hp, albeit at 1,800rpm – but torque figures were practically identical. In fact, in terms of specification, the two models were largely inseparable with horsepower and hydraulic flow the only obvious differences.

Farmers looking for a replacement for their venerable 135s were drawn to the tractors because, despite being 'new', they were a known quantity. The transmission and styling may have been different, but the technology was pure 135, which, as we all know, is no bad thing!

David Harrison uses his tidy MB trac 1600 Turbo as part of his agricultural contracting business. Photo: Howard Sherren

Mercedes-Benz 1600 Turbo

Although the MB-trac had its origins in 1972 with the 65/70 model, it really moved on in leaps and bounds in the mid to late-1980s with the updated Turbo range of tractors.

These tractors, with the popular 156hp 1600 model in particular, pushed the technology available at the time to the limit. A six-cylinder, turbocharged engine was standard across the entire range, with power channelled through a 14-forward and 14-reverse speed transmission to equal-sized wheels.

The long-stroke engine produced excellent torque and a 40km/h top speed made the tractor a joy to use on the road, but it was the tractor's bi-directional capability that helped it to find favour among the agricultural fraternity. Contractors were

the biggest fans of the format, as the tractor's rear load space made it possible to mount a sprayer, or other implement, while keeping the three-point linkage free.

With the entire seat and controls able to turn inside the cab, the operator could use the tractor in 'reverse' with ease – particularly useful if he needed improved visibility for close-quarter operations. The Claas Xerion has recently taken the concept to a new level, but there is no doubt that the MB-trac and the Turbo range in particular, were the first true success story for tractors of this type.

The future

The continuing changes in technology have inevitably meant that tractors are no longer the primitive hauling machines of

old. Advances in electronics and hydraulics have pushed the tractor far beyond the realms of what was once thought possible and it is difficult to imagine what the agricultural machines of the future will look like. The tractor has evolved into a hybrid that is capable of undertaking many tasks – a machine that has the towing capacity of a heavy goods vehicle and the comfort of a modern car, while being able to travel between ploughing jobs at speeds that are twice that of tractors from 30 years ago.

There is no doubt that tractors from the 20th century will remain popular with collectors and restorers, but as technology progresses it is unclear whether the farm machinery of today will be restorable by the typical tractor enthusiast in the years to come. ∎

TECHNICAL PUBLICATIONS SERVICE LTD

5, Vines Avenue, London N3 2QD
Tel: 020 8349 1757 Fax: 020 8343 1218
Email: sales@tractormanuals.co.uk

Workshop Manuals for Tractors, Engines, ATVs & Chain Saws

Containing clear and concise repair instructions with photos, diagrams including fits, timings and tolerances.

Also available - operators manuals and many other books on general maintenance, Hydraulics, welding and a wide range of tractor books & DVDs

FORD	Ref
TW5/TW15/TW25/TW35+4WD	FO45
5000/5600/5610/6600/6610/6700 + 4WD)	
6710/7000/7600/7610/7700/7710+4WD)	FO42
3230/3430/3930/4630/4830 + 4WD	FO47
2810/2910/3910+4WD	FO43
2310/2600/2610/3600/)	
3610/4100/4110/4600/4610)	FO41
2000/3000/4000	FO31
1100/1200/1300/1500/17001900/2110	
1110/1210/1310/1510/1710/1910+4WD	FO44
1120/1220/1230/1520/1720/1920/2120	FO46
Series 2N/8N/9N (Ford/Ferguson)	FO4

MASSEY-FERGUSON	
MF675/690/698 + 4WD	MF41
MF265/275/290	MF43
MF365/375/390/390T/398 + 4WD	MF45
MF350/360/399 + 4WD	MF46
MF2645/2685/2725 + 4WD	MF44
MF230/240/250	MF42
MF135 (PERKINS 3.152 ENGINE)	
MF165 (PERKINS 4.203 ENGINE)	MF27
MF1010/1020 (Std & Hydro)	MF47
MF35 (3 & 4 Cyl)	MF14
TE20 (PETROL ENGINE VERSION ONLY)	FE2

CASE/IH	
7110/7120/7130/7140 (Magnum)+4WD	C40
5120/5130/5140 + 4WD	C41
2090/2290/2390/2590 + 4WD)	
2094/2294/2394/2594 + 4WD)	C37
1190/1290/1390/1490/1690 + 4WD)	
1194/1294/1394/1494/1594 + 4WD)	C36
235/255/275 + 4WD	C42
385/485/585/685/885+4WD	C39

JOHN DEERE	
4055/4255/4455/4555/4755//4955 + 4WD	JD60
4050/4250/4450/4650/4850 + 4WD	JD57
4030/4230/4430 + HFWD	JD50
3130/3(040/3140 + 4WD	JD56
2650/2850/3050 + 4WD	JD59
1020/2020/2030	JD37

PRICE PER MANUAL £19.90
Postage within UK £2.00 each

FORD	Ref
5640/6640/7740/7840/8240/8340+4W	FO48
Fordson Dexta/Super Dexta)	
Fordson Major/Power Major/Super Major)	FO201
8600/8700/9700/TW10/TW20/TW30+4WD	FO201A

MASSEY-FERGUSON	
MF65/1080/1100/1135/1155	MF201
MF175	MF202

JOHN DEERE	
1040/1140/2040/2140)	
4040/4240/4440/4640/4840	JD202
4020/5020	JD203

INTERNATIONAL	
684/784/884/HYDRO84 + 4WD	IH202
454/484/574/584/674	IH203
275/414/434/384/354/444	IH201

DAVID BROWN	
885/995/1210/1212/1410/1412 + 4WD	
770/780/880/990/1200	C203

KUBOTA	
L175/210/225/225DT/260/B5100D/B5100E/	
6100D/6100E/B6100HST-D/6100HST-E	
7100D/B7100HST-D/7100HST-EK/	
L185/235/245/275/295/305/345/355	K201

ZETOR	
8011/8045/12011/12045	Z1
6045/7045/5011/6011/7011	Z2
4911/5911/5945/6911/6945	Z3
4712/4718/5711/5718/5745	
5748/6711/6718/6745/6748	Z4
2511/3511/4511/3545/3513	Z5
5211/5245/6211/6245	
7211/7245/7711/7745	Z6
8111/8145/10111/10145)	
12111/12145/16145)	Z7
8211/8245/9211/9245/10211/10245)	
11211/11245/12211/12245/14245/16245)	Z8
3320/3321/3340/3341/4320/4321)	
4340/4341/5320/5321/5340/5341)	
5340 Horal/6320/6321/6340/6341)	
6340 Horal/7321/7320/7340/7341)	Z9
9520/9540	Z10

PRICE PER MANUAL £26.00
Postage within UK £2.00 each

ATV REPAIR MANUALS

LEYLAND/NUFFIELD & BMC MINI	
245/262/272/282/462/472/482 Q Cab	Ref L3 £34.00
245/262/272/462/472 Std Cab (Pre 1977)	Ref L1 £34.00
285/2100	Ref L2 £34.00
Leyland 154	Ref L4 £25.00
Nuffield 10/42, 10/60. 3/45 & 4/65	Ref BM2 £25.00
Nuffield BMC Mini (Diesel & Petrol)	Ref BM1 £25.00
Postage within UK £3.50 EACH	

HONDA	Ref
ATC70/ATC90/ATC110/ATC125M/	
FOURTRAX·70/TRX125/FOURTRAX 125 (1970 - 1987)	M311
FOURTRAX 90/TRX90 (1993 - 2000)	M433
ATC185 AND 200 (1980 - 1986)	M326
FOURTRAX 200 SX ATC200X & (1986 - 1988)	M347
TRX250EX SPORTRAX (2001 - 2005)	M215
ODYSSEY FL250 (1977-1984)	M316
TRX200/ATC250 & FOURTRAX250 (19845- 1987)	M455
ATC250R (1981-1984)	M342
TRX250R/FOURTRAX 250R & ATC250R/(1985-1989)	M348
TRX250X/ TRX300EX FOURTRAX & SPORTRAX (1987 - 2006)	M456
TRX250 Recon and Recon ES (1997—2007)	M446
TRX300/FOURTRAX 2 & 4WD 300 /TRX 300FW/ (1988 - 2000)	M346
TRX350 RANCHER (2000 - 2006)	M200
TRX400EX FOURTRAX& SPORTRAX(1999-2007)	M454
TRX400FW/FOREMAN (1995 - 2003)	M459
TRX450E FOREMAN(1988 - 2004)	M205
TRX500FA RUBICON (2001-2004)/TRX500FGA (2004)	M210

KAWASAKI	
KLF220 Bayou (1988 - 2002) KLF 250 (2003)	M465
KSF250 Mojave (1987– 2004)	M385
KEF300 Lakota (1995 - 1999)	M470
KLF300 Bayou 2 & 4WD (1986 - 2004)	M466
KLF400 - Bayou (1993 - 1999)	M467

SUZUKI	Ref
ALT 125/LT125/ALT185/LT185 (1983 - 1987)	M381
LT230 & LT250 (1985 - 1990)	M475
LT 250R Quad Racer (1985 - 1992)	M380
LT-4WD/LT-4WDX/LT-F250 Quad Runner & King Quad (1987 - 1998)	M483
LT-Z400 (2003-2008)	M270
LTF500F (1998 - 2000)	M343

YAMAHA	
YFM80 Moto-4/YFM80 Badger (1985 - 2001)	M499
Raptor YFM660R (2001 - 2005)	M280
Raptor 700R (2006 - 2009)	M290
YTM200 /YTM225 and YFM200 (1985-1986)	M394
Blaster YFS200 (1988 - 2005)	M488
Timberwolf YFM250 & YFB250/YFB250FW (1989 - 2000)	M489
Warrior/YFM350X (1987 - 2004)	M487
Banshee YFZ 350 (1987 - 2006)	M486
Moto-4 & Big Bear -YFM350 2 & 4WD (1987-1999),	
YFM400 2 & 4WD (2000-2004)	M490
Kodiak YFM400FW (1993 - 1998)	M493
Grizzly 600 (2002 - 2008)	M285

POLARIS	
All 3, 4 & 6 wheel Drive Models (1985 - 1995)	M496
Magnum & Big Boss (1996 - 1999)	M362
Scrambler 500 4 x 4 (1997 - 2000)	M363
Polaris Sportsman 400 , 450 & 500 (1996 - 2008)	M365
Predator 500 (2003 - 2007)	M367

PRICE PER ATV MANUAL £24.50
Postage within UK £3.50 EACH

FOR FULL LISTING VISIT OUR WEBSITE
WWW.TRACTORMANUALS.CO.UK